Doctors in Opera

An Irreverent Look at Operatic Medicine

Dr J. Ian S. Robertson

Scottish
Opera

Dr J. Ian S. Robertson FRS(Edin.), MD, FRCP(Lond.), FRCP(Glas.), FAHA, FIBiol., BA(Manc.) is a former Professor of Medicine whose particular interests were in cardiology, hypertension, and endocrinology. Following retirement he gained a BA with first-class honours in Opera Studies at the University of Manchester. From 1999 to 2008 he was a member of the board of directors of Scottish Opera. He has written and lectured widely on medical aspects of opera.

Published by Scottish Opera

Scottish Opera
39 Elmbank Crescent
Glasgow G2 4PT

scottishopera.org.uk

A CIP record for this book is available from the British Library

ISBN 978-0-9572641-0-6

Reprint 1 2

The Letter libretto by Bernard MacLaverty, drawn from *Life and Fate* by Vasily Grossman.
Dr Ferret's Bad Medicine Roadshow libretto by Martin Riley.
We Come to the River by Hans Werner Henze is published by Schott.
The Man Who Mistook His Wife for a Hat by Michael Nyman is published by Chester Novello.

Front cover: *Der Rosenkavalier*, Scottish Opera, 2002. Photo: Bill Cooper.
Back cover: *Parsifal*, Scottish Opera, 2000. Photo: Bill Cooper.

Typeset in Garamond by Scottish Opera Graphics Department.

Printed and bound in Great Britain by 21 Colour, 21 Summerlee Street, Glasgow, G33 4DB.

CONTENTS

Preface v

1. Introduction: Doctors and Opera 1
2. Two Doctors, Two Apothecaries, and a Pharmacist 5
3. A Professor of Medicine 13
4. Three Surgeons 14
5. An Assiduous and Enterprising General Practitioner 18
6. Sexual Deprivation as a Cause of Mental Depression 21
7. Obstetrics and a Rash Prognosis 24
8. Two Cardiological Operas 25
9. Scottish Highland General Practice 29
10. Three Ophthalmologists 31
11. Welsh Rural General Practice 35
12. Psychiatry Through the Centuries 40
13. Doctors Who Fail to Examine the Patient 48
14. Four Plastic Surgeons 48
15. An Alcoholic Family Doctor 58
16. General Anaesthesia 61
17. A Silent General Practitioner 64
18. Three Quack Doctors 66
19. A Hospital Intern 70
20. Two Research Doctors 72
21. A Fraudulent General Practitioner 78
22. A Medicinal Chemist 80
23. A Canine General Practitioner 82
24. A Private Physician 83
25. The Mysterious Death of a Writer 85
26. A Resident Family Doctor and a Mistaken Diagnosis 87
27. A Doctor Assaulted 90
28. A Doctor Murdered 92
29. Some More Medical Impostors 94
30. Another Mistaken Diagnosis 101

31. Doctors as Politicians 103
32. A Very Brief and Over-Optimistic Medical Claim 108
33. Doctor as Philanderer 110
34. A Wife Mistaken for a Hat 113
35. A General Practitioner's Nightmare 116
36. Eccentricity, Rabies, and Possession by the Devil 117
37. Two Downtrodden Personal Physicians 120
38. The Administrator and the Waiting List 123
39. A Cancer Therapist and the Consequences of Inadequate Medication 125
40. A Hospital Death 127
41. An Imprudent General Practitioner 128
42. A Monk as Physician 130
43. An Evil Doctor 132
44. Envoi 135

Index of Operas 136

PREFACE

This book had its origins in a series of talks I was invited to give to the Senior Fellows of the Royal College of Physicians and Surgeons of Glasgow. These lectures were later extended to various branches of The Friends of Scottish Opera, then to the Royal College of Surgeons of Edinburgh, and to the Royal Philosophical Society of Glasgow. Especially gratifying was that from 2002 I was privileged to be invited annually to address the Buxton Festival Society at their Autumn Opera Weekend. The Buxton Friends have been especially generous in encouraging me to publish these thoughts and observations.

Although I am not aware of any previous venture of the present kind and scope, several authors have approached aspects of operatic medicine, usually, but not invariably, more reverently and soberly than I have here.

Linda and Michael Hutcheon, respectively a teacher of English and a physician, wrote their book *Opera: Desire, Disease, Death*[1] so as 'to combine medical and cultural history with literary and dramatic analyses', hoping 'that this "concord" might add ... to the understanding of opera's social and artistic impact'. Their work was therefore very different in its aims, scope, and style from mine.

Others have written articles on various medical aspects of opera. Lock[2] provided a succinct, accurate review of the topic. Dauber,[3] as is discussed in more detail in the present text, offered a thoughtful case study of Antonia in *The Tales of Hoffmann*. Carmody[4] considered that 'Doctors in opera ... seem determined to prove the truth of Dr Johnson's aphorism that opera is an exotic and irrational entertainment'. St Louis[5] analysed three 20th-century operas to demonstrate divergent approaches to the doctor-patient relationship. Willich[6] studied operatic physicians taken variously from the 18th, 19th, and 20th centuries and reflected on the changing public perceptions of medicine and medical practitioners over the years. That topic was also dealt with in some detail by Estes.[7] O'Donnell[8] comes closest to my irreverent approach, commenting that operatic doctors are 'wholly unacceptable role models'. As I hope to demonstrate here, that observation is substantially, but not entirely, correct.

Other professions have not been neglected in this regard. In 1995, Anthony J. Burgess published a beautifully produced, sumptuously illustrated account of *The Notary in Opera*.[9] I am not aware of any similar approach to operatic priests and parsons, although that appears to me to be an enticing topic for anyone sufficiently resolute to address it.

The account that follows is, as will be evident, derived mainly from my own (often very free) interpretation of the scores, libretti and programme books of the operas, and of the plays, poems, and books which I cite. I have further derived material from a wide range of publications written or edited by others.[10-21]

This present volume does not claim to be comprehensive. Any such attempt would in any case be futile from the outset, given the presumably very numerous operas which have been largely or wholly forgotten. Moreover, Estes discussed 'Dr' Crispino in the Riccis' *Crispino e la comare*, 'Dr' Callimaco in Castelnuovo-Tedesco's *La mandragola*, and two doctors in Giordano's *Fedora*, none of which I included in my lectures or describe further in the present text. Several of the operas listed by Willich are of questionable relevance and I have omitted them. I hope, nevertheless, not to have overlooked too many well-known works.

It should be evident from my text that discography would not be appropriate.

I express my profound gratitude to the people who have helped, advised, and encouraged me in the production of this book: Alex Reedijk, General Director of Scottish Opera; Derek Clark, Head of Music, Scottish Opera; Anne Higgins, Friends' Manager, Scottish Opera; The Buxton Festival staff and Friends; Patricia Hay, opera singer and Senior Vocal Lecturer at the Royal Conservatoire of Scotland; Derek Watson, writer and musicologist; Dr Stephen Lock; Dr Richard Dunstan; and the late Dr Freddy Fairhead. My especial thanks are due to my editor, Ian Brooke, and designer, Fiona Gauld; Miss Lesley Cook for dedicated secretarial work; and to Mignon for assiduous proof-reading. Any remaining errors are entirely my own.

1. Hutcheon, L. and Hutcheon, M., *Opera: Desire, Disease, Death*. University of Nebraska Press, Lincoln, USA, 1996.
2. Lock, S., 'Opera'. In *The Oxford Illustrated Companion to Medicine*, edited by Lock, S., Last, J.M. and Dunea, G., Oxford University Press, Oxford, 2001, pp. 593–4.
3. Dauber, L.G., 'Death in Opera: A Case Study', *American Journal of Cardiology*, 1992; 70: 838–40.
4. Carmody, J., 'Doctors and Opera', *The Medical Journal of Australia*, 1991; 155: 783–4.
5. St Louis, E.K., 'The Physician in Contemporary Opera', *The Pharos*, Spring 1992: 15–20.
6. Willich, S.N., 'Physicians in Opera – Reflection of Medical History and Public Perception', *British Medical Journal*, 2006; 333: 1333–5.
7. Estes, J.W., 'The Changing Role of the Physician in Opera', *Opera Quarterly*, 1994: 10: 142–55.
8. O'Donnell, M., 'On Not Giving a Figaro', *Health and Ageing*, November 2000: 48.
9. Burgess, A.J., *The Notary in Opera*, Jardine Press, Hadleigh, Suffolk, 1995.
10. Sadie, S. (ed.), *The New Grove Dictionary of Opera* (4 vols). Macmillan, London, 1992.
11. Holden, A. (ed.), *The Penguin Opera Guide*. Penguin Books, London, 1995.
12. Kennedy, M. (ed.), *The Concise Oxford Dictionary of Music*. Oxford University Press, Oxford, 1996.
13. Newman, E., *More Opera Nights*. Putnam, London, 1954.
14. Osborne, C., *The Complete Operas of Verdi*. Gollancz, London, 1978.
15. Budden, J., *The Operas of Verdi* (3 vols). Oxford University Press, New York, 1973.
16. Stuckenschmidt, H.H., *Arnold Schoenberg: His Life, World and Work*. Translated by H. Searle. John Calder, London, 1977.
17. Keates, J., *Handel: The Man and His Music*. Gollancz, London, 1985.
18. Jolliffe, J., *Glyndebourne: An Operatic Miracle*. John Murray, London, 1999.
19. Blythe, R. (ed.), *Aldeburgh Anthology*. Faber & Faber, London, 1972.
20. Hall, S.G., *Comedy in Context: Essays on Molière*. University Press of Mississippi, Jackson, USA, 1984.
21. Gibbon, E., *The Decline and Fall of the Roman Empire*, 1788.

1

INTRODUCTION: DOCTORS AND OPERA

This book presents a selection of doctors as they are portrayed on the operatic stage. Operatic doctors are predominantly, but not always, men, and they frequently appear ridiculous, or professionally incompetent, or venal. Often all three adjectives apply simultaneously. Voltaire's derogatory epigram, to the effect that the healing art comprises pouring drugs of which the doctor knows little into a body of which he knows less, is true of many medical operatic situations. Perhaps fortunately for our self-respect, occasionally operatic doctors are presented in more flattering aspect.

Further generalisations can be made. Doctors as operatic characters are most often basses or baritones, although there occur a fair number of tenors. Where doctors appear en masse, as in Massenet's *Cendrillon* or Prokofiev's *The Love for Three Oranges*, they are sung by a male chorus. Three operas, Sir Peter Maxwell Davies' *The Doctor of Myddfai* (1996), *The Letter* (2010) by Vitaly Khodosh, and Stephen Deazley's *Dr Ferret's Bad Medicine Roadshow* (2011), have a female doctor, respectively a soprano, mezzo-soprano, and mezzo-soprano. Occasionally operatic doctors have only a speaking part. Some doctors appearing in opera are wholly silent. Even a silent female doctor appears in Gareth Williams' *White* (2009). Complete silence in doctors is of course a quality many might regard as highly commendable.

Before I proceed to a consideration of the portrayal of doctors as characters in opera, I should point out in the partial defence of medical men and women that they have influenced opera in a variety of other ways. Many such beneficial contributions have been made by lapsed doctors, that is, by those who may once have obtained a medical qualification, but who have discovered subsequently more interesting, important, or remunerative pursuits.

Leopold Damrosch (1832–85) studied at Berlin University, then abandoned a career in medicine in favour of music. His opera *Romeo und Julia* was performed in Breslau in 1862. He was also a notable operatic conductor but is perhaps better known as the father of the (naturalised) American conductor and composer Walter Damrosch.

Alexander Borodin (1833–87) earned a doctorate in medicine at the St Petersburg Academy of Medicine. He later devoted himself to chemistry in which he had a most distinguished career. He was professor at the Medico-Surgical Academy at St Petersburg from 1864, and in 1872 administered a medical curriculum for women, an especially notable activity in Tsarist Russia. His professional duties were so onerous that his musical interests had to be relegated to his spare time. Borodin composed parts of four operas, of which the best known is *Prince Igor*, completed and orchestrated by Rimsky-Korsakov and Glazunov in 1890.

Bogumil Zepler,[1] a native of Breslau and a qualified doctor, turned in 1886 to musical composition, and between then and his death in 1918 wrote at least five operas, now almost forgotten, with much of the orchestration contributed by Arnold Schönberg.

The Scottish composer William Wallace (1860–1940) graduated in medicine from Glasgow University, later abandoning medicine for music, although he did return briefly to his erstwhile medical specialty, ophthalmology, during the First World War. Wallace's numerous compositions included no operas, but his perceptive writings often dealt with opera, and especially with Wagner. (His Irish namesake, William Vincent Wallace (1812–65), who was not medical, did compose operas).

The impresario Louis Véron (1798–1867) was in charge of the Paris Opéra from 1831 to 1835. Véron had earlier made a substantial fortune from the sales of a medicinal paste, which, when applied to the chest, purported to cure the common cold. At that time he was often referred to as 'Dr Véron', although he almost certainly did not possess a genuine medical qualification. As, a century and more later, there remains no cure for the common cold, the venture speaks well for Véron's commercial acumen, if not for his ethical probity.

Dr Tom Walsh, who *did* possess a medical qualification, founded the Wexford Opera Festival in 1951.

Leopold Damrosch, Giuseppe Sinopoli and Jeffrey Tate are medical men who took up operatic conducting. Dr Boyd Neel[2] conducted the very first operas to be performed in the newly constructed Glyndebourne opera house in March 1934. This was a private performance of three one-act works: Bach's *Coffee Cantata*, Mozart's *Bastien und Bastienne*, and Pergolesi's *La serva padrona*.

Another former doctor, Jonathan Miller, became an operatic producer.

Among medical men become singers, Alfred von Bary (1873–1926) deserves especial mention. Von Bary specialised in neurology until the age of 30, when his vocal ability was discovered and cultivated. He developed into an accomplished heldentenor, performing several major Wagner roles at Bayreuth between 1904 and 1914. Von Bary suffered from visual impairment, and it is alleged, rather implausibly, that he had to be guided about the stage by thick chalk marks inscribed thereon. This seems unlikely, since he would presumably have had to observe the conductor's directions. However, von Bary was obliged to retire from opera in 1918 because of near blindness, returning then to the practice of neurology. What his patients felt about being confronted by a physician who could hardly see them is not recorded. James Gilchrist is a contemporary doctor become operatic tenor.

The musicologist and biographer of Wagner, Curt von Westernhagen,[3] claimed that his medical training facilitated especial insight into the idiosyncracies of that composer, while rendering moralising less likely.

Ashton Ellis abandoned medical practice so as to devote himself to the English translation of Wagner's prose works, a venture arduous, yet but modestly successful. Many of the products of those labours still seem as though written in a foreign tongue.

Doctors have further made a most notable impact on this theatrical art form through their literary works being adapted as operatic libretti. Three operas, the two on *Wozzeck* by Berg and by Gurlitt, and Britten's *Peter Grimes*, were composed to libretti based on the literary works of medical men, respectively Georg Büchner in the case of the first two and by George Crabbe in the third. Interestingly, each of these operas also contains a doctor as a character. Another of Büchner's writings provided the story for Sitsky's opera *Lenz* and Rihm's opera *Jakob Lenz*. The Glasgow general practitioner Margaret McCartney wrote the libretto for Gareth Williams' *White*, which is set in a hospital.

My approach in this book is, however, rather differently to examine the professional and the musico-dramatic impact of medical men and women as they appear as characters on the operatic stage. Sometimes such operatic doctors are central to the action; on other occasions they have a minor or marginal role. As shall be seen, their skills and integrity vary widely.

My personal account is an uneven one, for which I make no apologies. The treatment of doctors by librettists is, in any event, also distinctly disparate. I have indulged a tendency to digress into sometimes only tenuously related topics as driven by whim. Mesmerism, and doctors as politicians are two such instances. I have furthermore not hesitated to impose my own interpretation of an operatic text whenever that seemed to me to be helpful. Tippett's *The Knot Garden* is one example. Such a relaxed, indulgent approach would of course be wholly inappropriate, indeed improper, in scientific medical writing. Emendation of that kind was even obligatory when I was confronted by several different operas derived from a particular literary source, as with *Romeo and Juliet*, *The Fall of the House of Usher*, and *The Scarlet Letter*. Conversely, of the numerous operas based on Shakespeare's *The Merry Wives of Windsor*, I have focused on just Verdi's *Falstaff*.

That I have occasionally exercised some narrative licence in my interpretation of libretti will no doubt provide operatic pedants with opportunity for criticism. I plead in proleptic exculpation that my adjustments have been modest in comparison with those of some contemporary exponents of Regietheater.

I have restricted myself to a consideration of doctors as characters specified in the libretti. The whims of producers (I have for example seen recently productions of Handel's *Orlando* and of Purcell's *The Fairy Queen* set in mental institutions) I have taken as beyond my scope. I have disregarded operatic appearances of Apollo, the classical god of medicine.

I have to make clear that, despite numerous representations I have received to the contrary, the character Faust was a necromancer and/or philosopher, but not a doctor of medicine. Thus I have excluded the numerous operas based on the Faust legend. Pietro von Abano, a necromancer in Spohr's 1827 opera of that name, and Albarn's Dr Dee, sorcerer and alchemist, are likewise omitted.

Perhaps perversely, I have however embraced several quacks and impostors; also some apothecaries who, in the 18th century, were involved in medical care. Also included is Dr Bartolo, and the five operas which concern him, despite several advisers arguing that he is not medical. However, his creator, Beaumarchais, made very clear that Dr Bartolo was 'a physician from Seville'. I have additionally touched on Wagner, who, despite having no doctors in any of his operas, dealt extensively with medical problems.

1. Zepler. See Preface note 16, p. 51.
2. Boyd Neel. See Hughes, S., *Glyndebourne*. Methuen, London, 1965, p. 47.
3. Von Westernhagen, C., *Wagner*. Translated by M. Whittall. Cambridge University Press, Cambridge, 1978, p. xv.

TWO DOCTORS, TWO APOTHECARIES, AND A PHARMACIST

DITTERSDORF: DOCTOR AND APOTHECARY 1786

I propose to begin by considering one of the earliest operas to feature a doctor in its cast list. This is *Doctor and Apothecary* by Carl Ditters von Dittersdorf, dated Vienna 1786, and composed to a libretto by Gottlieb Stephanie the Younger after a French drama *L'apothicaire de Murcie* by 'Le Compte N—'. The French count was evidently rather a reticent gentleman. I shall examine here the social consequences of professional animosity.

Crucial to an understanding of this operatic plot is an appreciation of the prevalent 18th- century mutual ill-feeling between professional medical men ('proper doctors' as they liked to be called) and apothecaries, which provides the background circumstances of Dittersdorf's opera. The action takes place in a small German or Austrian town in the mid-18th century. In that central European town there exists a bitter professional, and hence personal, feud between the local apothecary and quack Stössel (bass) and the physician Doctor Krautmann (baritone). However, as so often happens in opera, love intervenes and here love disrupts the established well-ordered enmity between those two rival practitioners of the healing arts.

Leonore, a soprano, the daughter of the apothecary Stössel, has fallen in love with Gotthold, tenor (Gotthold is an operatic lover, and hence is obliged to be a tenor). And Gotthold, the lover, is the son of Doctor Krautmann, Stössel's sworn enemy. But Stössel and his wife Claudia (contralto) have other ideas; they wish to marry off their daughter instead to Captain Sturmwald, another tenor, a wounded, disfigured, and alcoholic ex-army officer.

Even allowing for the ill-feeling between the Doctor and the Apothecary, this is distinctly odd. Responsible parents would usually be inclined to steer their marriageable daughters well away from army officers of any kind; certainly away from erratic alcoholic invalids such as the retired Captain Sturmwald. To most parents the Doctor's son would in such circumstances appear to be a much preferable alternative. Here, however, Stössel and his wife take a different view. We have to remember of course that the librettist must provide a serviceable operatic plot. Very likely the librettist here, Gottlieb Stephanie the Younger, was driven more by musico-dramatic necessity than by literary common sense. At any rate, that is the course taken by this librettist. The social circumstances and hence the drama are further complicated in that Sichel (tenor), a young friend of the Doctor's son Gotthold, has fallen in love with the Apothecary's niece Rosalia (soprano). Hence the two male would-be suitors are from the Doctor's entourage; the two young ladies they are wooing are from the family of the Doctor's bitter rival and enemy, the apothecary Stössel. This provides of course, as the librettist no doubt intended, a most fertile soil for operatic comedy.

The initial ploy of the Doctor's son Gotthold and his friend Sichel is to lure Stössel away by playing on his professional pride and financial avarice, and deceitfully informing him that his medical services, such as they are, are needed on the other side of the town. However, their consequent contrived tryst with the two young ladies is interrupted by the appearance of Stössel's wife Claudia, then further disrupted by the arrival of Captain Sturmwald, and finally by the return of the now irate Stössel himself. The two blades, the intending lovers, are obliged to retreat in some confusion.

The second attempt at infiltration by the two young men is more imaginative, highly improbable, but nonetheless successful. The Doctor's son Gotthold now disguises himself as a notary, his friend Sichel even more outlandishly as Captain Sturmwald. And by way of these subterfuges the signatures of the unwitting Stössel and Claudia are secured on marriage contracts uniting the Doctor's son Gotthold with their daughter Leonore; and his chum Sichel with their niece Rosalia. The obvious legal anomaly of the notary being an unqualified impostor is deftly sidestepped by the librettist and does not affect the outcome.

The two fathers, Apothecary Stössel and Doctor Krautmann, are initially furious at this deception. But then Stössel's wife Claudia has a miraculously rational change of heart, pointing out the considerable professional and hence financial benefits to accrue if the presently opposing families cooperate rather than squabble, and so the two pairs of lovers are sensibly welcomed and happily united. The wounded veteran Captain Sturmwald is left to continue his drunken invalidism still as a bachelor.

Aside from the medical aspects, this is a work of considerable interest in operatic history. One noteworthy feature is that *Doctor and Apothecary* is a German-language Singspiel, that is, sections of spoken dialogue are interspersed with the musical numbers. The Austrian Emperor Joseph II was enthusiastically bent on creating in Vienna a national Singspiel company. Joseph's attempt began in 1778, and included Mozart's *Die Entführung aus dem Serail* of 1782. *Doctor and Apothecary*, first performed in 1786, helped Joseph to revive his venture which had, by that latter date, begun to falter.

Musically and dramatically, of especial significance is the multisectional finale to Act I, replacing what was, up to that time, the more conventional so-called vaudeville ending. With a vaudeville ending each main character sings a stanza in turn, with the full ensemble joining in the refrain. Mozart's operas *Die Entführung* of 1782 and *Der Schauspieldirektor* of 1786 have typical vaudeville endings. Dittersdorf's long and very different multisectional finale here, to which Captain Sturmwald, who has fallen asleep drunk, contributes loud snoring, is thought by some commentators possibly to have been inspired by the finale to Act II of Mozart's *The Marriage of Figaro*, which was first performed, and certainly seen by Dittersdorf, earlier in that same year, 1786. However, if that explanation is correct, Dittersdorf would have had to move fast. *The Marriage of Figaro* had its premiere performance in May 1786; *Doctor and Apothecary* in July of that year. I am therefore inclined to doubt the notion that Dittersdorf got the idea from Mozart, and hence Dittersdorf deserves I believe some credit for that originality of musical construction.

BRITTEN: PETER GRIMES 1945

Dr George Crabbe, upon whose poem the libretto of this opera is based, was born in 1754. Thus he was two years older than Mozart and five years older than Robert Burns. However, Crabbe lived until 1832, much longer than those two more famous contemporaries, both of whom died in the 1790s.

Crabbe's birthplace was Aldeburgh, which was then, and remains, a small fishing town on the coast of Suffolk. It was in Aldeburgh where he was brought up, and where for some years he had his medical practice. Crabbe's father appears to have combined the duties of customs official, warehouseman, and schoolteacher. A picture in the town museum at Aldeburgh purports to be of George Crabbe's birthplace. The appearance is of a rather humble dwelling, although not so humble as that of Burns, as is evident from a comparison with Burns' cottage at Alloway in Ayrshire. A photograph in a book edited by Ronald Blythe[1] and entitled *Aldeburgh Anthology* shows a decaying hulk in the water at Slaughden, Aldeburgh, and is captioned 'Where Crabbe worked' when young. It could be a picture of the docks where Crabbe did work briefly; alternatively it could be intended simply to convey the ambience of that part of Aldeburgh. If I am wrong on both counts, I am obliged to conclude that general practitioners' surgeries in the latter part of the 18th century were even less well appointed than they are today.

As well as being a doctor George Crabbe was a poet, and his poetry repeatedly reveals his dissatisfaction with the practice of medicine and his sense of inadequacy as a medical practitioner. Thus in his poem *The Parish Register* we find:

> Sick lies the man, bewildered, lost, afraid,
> His spirits vanquished and his strength decayed;
> No hope his friend, the nurse, the doctor lend –
> Call then a priest and fit him for his end.

Whatever else, the practice of medicine does require a measure of psychological toughness, and if that can be combined with some optimism, which latter can then be transmitted to the patient, so much the better. These are, however, qualities which Crabbe seems always to have lacked. Thus it is no surprise that he abandoned medicine for the Church and in 1782 became ordained as a clergyman in the Church of England. He claimed that the translation offered him three advantages. Two of those claims I am ready to accept, although the third I regard as more questionable. The first was that as a parson he had more time to write poetry; I have no problem with that. Second, the remuneration was greater and more secure with the Church; that again I am confident is true. Third, he regarded the profession of clergyman as more upright and ethical than that of doctor. That last claim I would dispute, though I might of course be wrong.

Crabbe's poetry shows further that when in medical practice he, like Doctor Krautmann, bore a marked aversion to apothecaries, who were in England at that time in fact virtually quacks. Such charlatans required no qualifications and were under no legal restraint. In Crabbe's view they frequently maltreated their customers; they also diverted patients and hence income from him. In his poem *The Village* he describes:

> A potent quack, long versed in human ills,
> Who first insults the victim whom he kills;
> Whose murderous hand a drowsy bench protect
> And whose most tender mercy is neglect.

The opera deriving from Crabbe's literary work is Benjamin Britten's *Peter Grimes*, which was composed to a libretto by Montagu Slater after Crabbe's poem *The Borough*, 'The Borough' being the town of Aldeburgh itself. This opera features a general practitioner, George Crabbe himself in a silent part, and just such an apothecary, the baritone role of Ned Keene, as the real Dr Crabbe so despised.

A familiar photograph depicts the composer sitting on a breakwater by the beach, with the caption stating: 'Britten at home in Aldeburgh'. Again, I believe this information is intended in a general topographical rather than a specific domiciliary sense. I have visited two of the houses in which at different times Britten lived in Aldeburgh. Both are more soundly built than is the structure depicted in that photograph.

Peter Grimes, the central character in the opera, is a local Aldeburgh fisherman. He is able, aloof, eccentric, and different. And to be different in Aldeburgh is condemnation enough, now as then. Grimes has the particular misfortune to have two of his apprentices die by accident on separate occasions. Largely in consequence, he is persecuted by the townspeople and driven first to madness and finally to suicide. The tenor role of Peter Grimes is musically interesting in that it can be, and has been, sung by various styles of singer, from heldentenor to light lyric tenor. In all Aldeburgh, Peter Grimes has only two friends; a retired sea captain, Balstrode, a baritone part, and the widowed schoolteacher, Ellen Orford, soprano. Ellen Orford is in love with him, but he never proposes to her.

Dr George Crabbe himself has in the opera an important yet silent role (he is 'Dr Thorp' in some early productions because directors were then worried about possible anachronism). In one scene he is for example shown moving quietly among the fisherfolk who are pursuing the activities normally undertaken by such people when not at sea – gutting fish, repairing nets, and smoking clay pipes. Crabbe there carries his notebook, making observations for future incorporation into his poems just as the real Dr Crabbe would have done. Although he never speaks or sings in the opera, others address him: 'Goodnight Dr Crabbe!'; 'Come along Doctor!', and so forth. In Act I, as Dr Crabbe heads into The Boar Inn, the tenor Bob Boles calls mockingly after him: 'He drinks "Good health" to all diseases.'

In the opera the baritone Ned Keene, an unlicensed apothecary, is, among other activities, a drug-pusher for the opium addict and gossip, Mrs Sedley. Mrs Sedley, sung by a mezzo-soprano, is in the opera an especial adversary of Peter Grimes. Interestingly, the real Dr Crabbe seems to have himself been partial to opium.

The Elizabethan Moot Hall stands in Aldeburgh today near the waterfront as it did in George Crabbe's time. The Moot Hall features several times in the opera. In the Prologue it is the scene of the inquest on the first of Grimes' apprentices to die by accident. Then, at the end, after a second apprentice has fallen to his death, and Peter Grimes has been driven out of his wits, Captain Balstrode reluctantly decides that the only avenue left is Grimes' suicide. So Balstrode tells the deranged man to sail his boat out to sea until he can no longer see the Moot Hall, and then to 'sink her'. Grimes has just sufficient comprehension to absorb this, and to comply, and so dies by his own hand. And the inhabitants of Aldeburgh proceed unconcernedly about their workaday affairs.

There are in Aldeburgh today several memorials to George Crabbe. Thus there is Crabbe House, where he is supposed to have lived at one time; also Crabbe Street, near where the public lavatories are situated. Similar monuments to Benjamin Britten have been by comparison more grudging, although there has been for several years a plaque on the wall of a house where he formerly stayed. But in 2003 that was to change.

Britten's devotees commissioned an artwork intended to be erected publicly in his memory. There is a delightful symmetry in this – not in the work as such, but in the circumstances of its genesis. Benjamin Britten was an acknowledged homosexual; the sculpture was executed by Maggi Hambling, an outspoken lesbian. The symmetry extends further, however. The proponents of this work indicated several locations in Aldeburgh where they would be pleased to see it situated; the opponents stated no less forcibly where they could put it.

The enthusiasts evidently prevailed; the work was installed on Aldeburgh north beach and was unveiled on Saturday 8 November 2003. That event was recorded by the art critic and commentator Andrew Lambirth.[2] To describe Lambirth's prose as purple would be to understate the case substantially. It is beyond purple, indeed of a much deeper hue. Thus: 'the clouds lowered and the waves surged ... overwhelmed by the ravishing beauty of the piece and its triumphant suitability ... fragmented scallop-shell forms rearranged to make a winged yet grounded object ... subtly ridged and curved steel ... quivers sensually in the high wind from the North Sea. The dappled patina of the surfaces, and the play of internal forms to outward silhouette ... ever-changing profile ... at the very moment of the unveiling, the sun came out in great Blakean trapeziums (sic) of gold'. And then we were at once plunged into bathos, because this account was accompanied by a photograph showing Maggi Hambling sitting on the thing, smoking a fag.

In all of this we have, of course, to recognise a fundamental difference between Crabbe and Britten. Crabbe was born and brought up in Aldeburgh, and for many years he had his medical practice there. By contrast, Britten, although he conferred much fame on the town, was an outsider. Britten had been born not in Aldeburgh but in Lowestoft, some 30 miles along the coast.

DONIZETTI: IL CAMPANELLO DI NOTTE 1836

I propose now to contrast the behaviour and standing of the two preceding apothecaries with those of a clearly conscientious pharmacist although, as shall be seen, even when professional behaviour is throughout impeccable, it may excite only derision on the operatic stage. The opera is Donizetti's *Il campanello di notte* of 1836, composed to his own libretto after the vaudeville *La sonnette de nuit* by Brunswick, Troin, and Lhérie.

Don Annibale Pistacchio, sung by a buffo bass, is a middle-aged gentleman who has hitherto been a bachelor. He is in charge of a pharmacy in Naples. The opera opens at his wedding reception, he having just married the soprano Serafina. As Don Annibale rather severely points out, under Neapolitan law a fully qualified pharmacist, and he only, is permitted to make up prescriptions. Should there be patients ringing the night bell, he will, however reluctantly, arise from the marriage bed and attend to their needs. This exchange has rather imprudently been conducted within earshot of Enrico, baritone, an earlier, and obviously now disappointed, suitor of Serafina. Enrico determines to disrupt the consummation of the marriage by making repeated visits as an impostor to the pharmacy through the night. This being opera, we in the audience perceive at once that every one of these nocturnal customers is Enrico in disguise, yet each time Don Annibale is deceived.

Enrico's first manifestation as a ringer of the night bell is in the form of a French dandy, who has eaten and drunk too well, and to excess. Thus he has, according to his own account, consumed thirty ice creams, washed down by several bottles of malaga, champagne, and port. Hardly surprisingly, he is now

Il campanello: Enrico (Leo Nucci), posing as an elderly husband, confronts Don Annibale Pistacchio (Enzo Dara) with a lengthy prescription. Spiridione, Don Annibale's assistant (here the tenor Luca Casalin) tries to help. Teatro Regio Torino, 1995. Photo: Davide Peterle © Teatro Regio Torino.

embarrassed by flatulence, which he proceeds to describe, in disgustingly lengthy detail. After a protracted and partly acrimonious exchange, he is eventually sent off 'with a bottle'.

But before Don Annibale can get to bed there is another customer ringing the night bell; Enrico again, of course, this time in the form of an opera singer who has lost his voice. Don Annibale makes some attempt at polite conversation: 'Ah, this must be a new opera by that excellent composer Rossini?', 'Oh no! Donizetti!', 'Ah yes, of course, Donizetti – a delightful fellow' – and so on. Each proffered prescription has to be accompanied by a therapeutic trial, often lengthy, on the spot. There are several false starts before some suitably effective throat lozenges are provided, and the grateful singer goes on his way.

But still Don Annibale does not get to bed and his bride. There now appears in facsimile an elderly gentleman who has come not on his own behalf, but for his wife, who is herself too ill to attend. This is hardly surprising, because she is supposedly suffering from diabetes, as a consequence of which she is nearly blind; consumption; intestinal fistulae (seven in number); flatulence (again); a cerebral tumour; sciatica; and gout. The multiple prescriptions for all of these diseases clearly are going to need several hours to make up. Don Annibale is very conscientious, and he is rightly concerned not to prescribe mutually incompatible drugs (it is interesting to note how these old operas can sometimes have a vivid contemporary resonance). Surprisingly, it does not occur to Don Annibale to question why such an extensive requirement for medicines treating longstanding disorders needs to be made up in the middle of the night. He does persuade the old husband that all of this is going to take several hours, and he had best return in the morning to collect the medicines.

The work indeed takes all night, and Don Annibale never does get to bed. In the morning the revelling guests return, offering the usual coarse ribaldry supposedly appropriate to such occasions. The still virginal Don Annibale is not amused. He is obliged to his further annoyance to leave Naples that morning for Rome on legal business. The opera ends at that point, and we never do get to hear of the subsequent course of this marriage, which has had to endure such a frustrating beginning.

1. Blythe. See Preface note 19, p. 50.
2. *The Spectator,* 15 November 2003, p. 70.

3

A PROFESSOR
OF MEDICINE

BERG: LULU 1937/1979

Medical professorship is a branch of the profession usually regarded as hierarchically pre-eminent, and I thought it appropriate to consider a professor of medicine early in this volume. As shall be seen, however, no such esteem is afforded the operatic Professor of Medicine in *Lulu*. At the composer Alban Berg's death in 1935 he had completed Acts I and II of this opera, as well as the short score of Act III, which was however only partly orchestrated. The orchestration of Act III was finished by Friedrich Cerha in 1979. The libretto, by Berg himself, is based on two plays by Frank Wedekind, *Earth Spirit* and *Pandora's Box*.

The spoken role of the Professor of Medicine, who is the first of Lulu's several husbands, is brief and undistinguished. In Act I Scene 1 Lulu is having her portrait painted in the artist's studio. At the point when the Professor arrives to inspect progress Lulu and the Painter, behind a locked door, are making love. The Professor demands loudly that the door be opened, eventually forces it, sees what is going on, and drops dead. And that is almost, but not quite, the end of the Professor.

This is a strictly symmetrical opera. The first half depicts Lulu ascending the social scale; the second half her converse decline, ending with her as a common prostitute on the streets of London. Several of the characters in the two halves are mirror images of one another. The Professor of Medicine, Lulu's first husband, is reflected in the final scene by her first client, a preacher. However, as the latter has a wholly silent part, he is, I fear, even less distinguished operatically than his Act I counterpart.

Opposite: *Lulu:* Lulu (Beverly Morgan), The Painter (Justin Lavender), and the now-dead Professor of Medicine (Ian McKinven). Scottish Opera, 1987. Photo: Eric Thorburn.

THREE SURGEONS

Requiring some emphasis is that not all operatic doctors are forbidding, ethically dubious, or professionally incompetent. Of course, hardly surprisingly, when we seek professional probity and skill on the operatic stage, we most readily find those qualities displayed by a surgeon. However, as shall be seen in the second of the three operas recounted here, surgical fame and prestige can be precarious.

VERDI: LA FORZA DEL DESTINO 1862/1869

I shall consider first *La forza del destino* (*The Force of Destiny*) by Giuseppe Verdi, to a libretto by the Italian Piave, who derived his text from two plays, *Don Alvaro* by the Spanish playwright Rivas, and *Wallenstein's Camp* by the German, Schiller. The opera first appeared in 1862, and was then revised by Verdi in 1869. This is a long opera, with an involved plot, into which fortunately it is unnecessary to enter in detail for my present purposes. In summary, before the short scene that shall now be described, Don Alvaro, the lead tenor, has supposedly seduced Leonora, soprano, the sister of Don Carlos, baritone, and that ruined sister has been obliged to retire to a convent. For good measure, Don Alvaro has also murdered, or at least is believed to have murdered, the father of Don Carlos and Leonora. At the present moment, however, Don Carlos is unaware that Don Alvaro is the culprit who has committed these crimes; the two of them are fellow officers in the army and great friends.

There is a battle. As can readily be appreciated, portraying a full-scale 19th-century battle on the theatrical stage would be both difficult and expensive. Verdi and his librettist get around this problem by having the surgeon, a tenor, observe and comment on events from a distance. It will be at once evident that this particular surgeon is of the taciturn variety, thus: 'The grenadiers are valiant! ... My God, he has fallen wounded! [The person who has fallen wounded is Don Alvaro.] ... Ah! Our soldiers are victorious!' And with those brief phrases there have been established some crucial facts, namely that the grenadiers are brave and skilled at warfare; that Don Alvaro has been wounded in the action; and that our chaps have won. The opera may now proceed.

Don Alvaro is borne in, wounded and unconscious, on a stretcher. His fellow-officer, Don Carlos, says: 'Gently – put him here'. The surgeon, however, is not having any of this. This is a medical matter, he is now in charge of affairs, and he proposes to establish the priorities straight away. So he says sharply: 'Be quiet!' There follows a fatuous enquiry from Don Carlos: 'Is he in any danger?' One might suppose that even a lay person could work out that someone who has just been shot on the battlefield and carted in unconscious is unlikely to be in particularly robust health. Note nevertheless the cunning wording of the surgeon's reply: 'The bullet in his chest causes me concern' (as it would, and should, of course). This is a cleverly cautious prognosis. It means that if Don Alvaro does die, any blame attaching to the surgeon will be limited. Conversely, if the surgeon should operate successfully, so much the greater will be the kudos. There then occurs a further gormless exhortation from Carlos: 'Oh save him!' (this is opera, after all). The surgeon and the orderlies carry the wounded man away.

This affords Don Carlos the opportunity to go through the belongings of Don Alvaro, in the course of which he discovers a locket containing a portrait of his sister Leonora. Thus are revealed the important matters of which he had previously been unaware, that Don Alvaro was the bounder who had seduced and ruined his sister, and had also been apparently the murderer of his father. This news understandably changes the attitude of Carlos to his erstwhile chum quite a lot, and he now expounds on what a rotter Alvaro is, how deceitful he has been, and proceeds to describe in considerable detail the various unpleasant things he proposes to do to Alvaro if the surgeon can restore him to reasonable working order.

All of this gives the surgeon time to complete his work, and he now reappears, laconic to the last: 'Good news; he is saved!' (He departs.) Carlos: 'Oh joy!' This expression of joy is not of course to be taken at face value. If Carlos is pleased, and that may be doubted, it is only to the extent that should Alvaro recover, he can be challenged to a duel, and the unfinished business of the disgraced sister and the murdered father can be settled. Towards the end of the opera just such a duel does indeed take place, but that, as they say, is another part of the story.

The surgeon here is certainly professionally skilful. His role in the opera is, however, modest, albeit, as should be readily perceived, pivotal to the dramatic construction.

HAAS: ŠARLATÁN 1938

I shall turn now to one of those rather unusual operas in which the doctor is the central figure. The opera here is *Šarlatán*, which the Czech composer Pavel Haas completed in 1938 to his own libretto after a tale by Josef Winkler. The doctor is a surgeon and is professionally skilled. Sadly, that expertise only briefly brings him the reward he deserves. However accomplished the surgical technique may be, careful post-operative supervision must always be undertaken. The surgeon here neglects that just once, to his own, and to the patient's, discomfiture.

The opera is set in central Europe at the time of the Thirty Years' War, that is, in the early 17th century. Thus the surgeon is styled 'Dr' Pustrpalk, not, as would be in the British fashion, 'Mr'. 'Šarlatán' is a Czech word which has exactly the same meaning as the English 'charlatan', leaving no doubt of the homiletic bias of the libretto.

Pustrpalk (baritone) is a travelling surgeon, who goes from town to town plying his trade, taking with him a special tent in which to perform his surgical operations. Because he is an itinerant surgeon, Pustrpalk requires to advertise his skills on arrival at each new venue, in a manner which would certainly not now be approved, at any rate in Britain. If his promotional account is to be believed, which almost surely it should not, certainly not in its entirety, he is a person of considerable accomplishments. Thus he has in the past performed successful xenotransplantation (transplantation of an organ from another species), replacing the severely diseased stomach of one of his patients with that of a goat. This was done with evident finesse, the only obvious post-operative problem being that the patient was obliged to consume a more omnivorously caprine diet than hitherto.

That, being a promotional account, may perhaps in certain particulars be doubted. Nevertheless, before the very eyes of the audience, Pustrpalk displays both medical skill and ethical integrity. Thus a boy presenting with a swollen painful face, requesting a dental extraction because of a supposed tooth abscess, is correctly diagnosed instead as having mumps, reassured that the condition is self-limiting, and sent on his way without fee. Another patient suffering snakebite has the venom successfully removed.

There is then witnessed one of Dr Pustrpalk's most dramatic medical achievements. He is asked to advise on Amaranta (mezzo-soprano), the young wife of a professor of medicine. Amaranta has been paraplegic, that is, paralysed from the waist down, following childbirth some months earlier. Her case has baffled her husband and his medical colleagues. She is examined by Dr Pustrpalk, who quickly perceives that her problem is psychiatric rather than organic. She is suffering from hysterical paralysis. Pustrpalk cures her, on stage, in appropriately dramatic fashion. He has her attendants carry her into the surgical tent. He then commands, very loudly: 'Off with her frilly knickers', at which there is a frisson through the audience and the on-stage chorus. He then orders: 'Up with her skirts', whereupon there is more salacious expectancy. And then, even more loudly: 'Plunge her into the hip-bath!' At this there is a scream, and Amaranta rushes from the tent, hastily rearranging her clothing and quite evidently restored. This Pustrpalk has achieved by having had the bath filled with stinging nettles.

Pustrpalk goes on to cure the King (bass) of lassitude and depression by giving him a tonic, at which the doctor is rewarded with money, honours, and medals, the equivalent and more of a knighthood for services to medicine today. All of this of course excites envy and jealousy from his rivals, thus once again closely replicating current susceptibilities.

Then, at the height of his fame, there follows disaster. Pustrpalk successfully performs a most difficult and intricate intestinal operation on a monk. He is relaxing with a drink, when his assistant rushes from the surgical tent to announce that the patient has suddenly died of a massive post-operative haemorrhage. Pustrpalk is at once denounced as a charlatan, one of his most vocal critics being the town physician (bass), and he is hounded from practice. A present-day parallel of this misfortune would be trial by tabloid newspapers. His demotion to obscurity for this understandable, if nonetheless culpable, lapse is prompt and final.

My own sympathies in all this nevertheless are with Pustrpalk. He is in my opinion among the best of operatic doctors, and he deserves I consider a better fate.

ALEXANDER RASKATOV: A DOG'S HEART 2009

Alexander Raskatov's opera *A Dog's Heart*, to a libretto by Cesare Mazzonis, is the most recent of at least three operas based on a satirical novel by Mikhail Bulgakov which was banned by Stalin in 1925. Others were *The Murder of Comrade Sharik* (1973) by William Bergsma, and *Heart of a Dog* (2007) by Rudolf Rojan.

In Raskatov's opera Philip Philopovich Preobrazhensky (baritone) is a distinguished Moscow surgeon whose specialty is rejuvenation by the transplantation into patients of various animal glands. He discovers in a cold wintry Moscow street a starving dog. The thoughts of the dog are conveyed variously via a soprano and countertenor.

Preobrazhensky entices the dog to his home with a sausage, feeds the dog up, and then transplants into the animal (now called Sharik = Fluffy) the testes and pituitary gland of a recently deceased criminal. Fluffy metamorphoses into a coarse, evil, self-serving brute, named Sharikov (cast-iron), performed by a tenor. That name clearly indicates that he is a caricature of Stalin (steel), and, hardly surprisingly, led to the suppression of the original novel.

The lavish English National Opera production of 2010 by Simon McBurney and designed by Michael Levine had twenty-three roles taken by eighteen soloists; four puppet-masters and their puppets (including a dog and several cats); twelve actors; and a large chorus.

The surgeon here, Preobrazhensky, like Dr Pustrpalk in *Šarlatán*, is notable in achieving successful xenotransplantation. These are impressive professional feats, but would be unlikely in real life, especially given the dates of the two tales. Both patients would almost certainly have rejected immunologically the foreign implanted tissue.

AN ASSIDUOUS AND ENTERPRISING GENERAL PRACTITIONER

JUDITH WEIR: A NIGHT AT THE CHINESE OPERA 1987

A Night at the Chinese Opera was Judith Weir's first full-length opera, composed to her own libretto after the 13th-century Chinese play *The Chao Family Orphan* by Chi Chun-hsiang. This musical work was remarkable for being at once hailed as a singular triumph. Very few composers have achieved success with their first opera; Judith Weir thus joined a very select group.

Also rather unusual, at any rate in opera, is that Judith Weir's doctor here is, both professionally and personally, a man of distinction, undertaking arduous and dangerous tasks well beyond the scope of strictly medical duties. He is Dr Ch'êng Ying, not an easy name to pronounce. Dr Ch'êng Ying, as shall be seen, has a crucial role in Act II of the opera, that Act II comprising a discrete play which is presented within the overall dramatic span of the opera. This play-within-a-play is given especial piquancy and humour in that it is enacted by a troupe of just three travelling players, a soprano, a tenor, and a mezzo-soprano. Since there are only three of them they are required to perform multiple roles. They attempt to convey clarity in this by announcing at each of their entrances exactly which character they are at that point intending to portray. I shall now attempt to present the essence, and especially the medical essence, of that Act II play-within-a-play, entitled *The Orphan of Chao*, which reflects, and emphasises, the supposedly real events of the two outer acts.

The wicked General Tu-an-ku schemes and plots, and proceeds to remove his rival for the Emperor's favour, the loyal civil servant Chao, together if he can with Chao's entire family. The bloodthirsty Tu-an-ku ruthlessly engineers the death of three hundred of Chao's relatives. Chao evidently has or had a very large extended family. As Tu-an-ku says by way of explanation: 'It is better to uproot the grass than cut it short'.

Then, by employing a forged document, Tu-an-ku induces Chao-the-loyal-civil-servant to commit suicide, which Chao does by stabbing himself on stage.

There is, as we shall see, plenty of blood spilt in this opera. In the 2008 Scottish Opera production the gory mess was, up to a point, contained, by having the torrents of freely spouting blood represented by ice-cube-sized chunks of scarlet foam thrown around the set.

Before he embarks on this suicide, Chao-the-loyal-civil-servant points to the swollen belly of his heavily pregnant wife, and instructs her: 'If it is a boy, let him be called "The Orphan of Chao": when he is a man, he shall avenge my death'. It is rather surprising that Chao is talking about an orphan at this stage. Chao himself certainly is about to die, but the wife so far seems healthy, albeit heavily pregnant. Chao then stabs himself and his wife drags his body off stage. Chao's wife does indeed give birth to a son, dread news to the wicked general Tu-an-ku, who resolves to kill the child. Enter the physician, Dr Ch'êng Ying.

Dr Ch'êng Ying attends the widow of Chao, and prescribes herbal medicines for her to take after her confinement. Suddenly the widow thrusts the baby into the Doctor's arms and rather surprisingly strangles herself. Dr Ch'êng Ying is left, as the old cliché has it, holding the baby, in every sense. The child now truly is an orphan. Dr Ch'êng Ying, clearly a resourceful man of decision, stuffs the baby into his medical black bag, partly covers the infant with his therapeutic herbs, and rushes away. The doctor is stopped by another, this time however more kindly, general, Han Chueh. Han Chueh discovers the baby, but rather unexpectedly, certainly commendably, takes pity on Dr Ch'êng Ying and the child. Han Chueh tells the doctor to hide the orphan away, to educate him, and especially to instruct him in the arts of war, so that the orphan may, when grown up, take revenge on the dastardly Tu-an-ku.

Han Chueh then, abruptly, and once again without warning, becomes the third suicide of Act II. He cuts his own throat and drops dead on stage. It is by now very clear that despite the evidently wide range of the doctor's professional skills, his talents do not include the prediction or prevention of suicide, or the resuscitation of patients intent on that course.

Dr Ch'êng Ying, clearly nonetheless unabashed, and still carrying the baby in his black bag, proceeds to the house of the very elderly Kung-Sun Ch'u-Chiu. (I have not made up these names; Judith Weir wrote the libretto.) Kung-Sun Ch'u-Chiu had also once been a civil servant, but since the rise of the ambitious and ruthless Tu-an-ku at the Emperor's court, he has abandoned that profession and he has taken up, as retired civil servants often do, pig farming. He greets Dr. Ch'êng Ying.

The vengeful Tu-an-ku is then heard approaching. The doctor quickly takes the baby from his medical black bag and rushes with the child into Kung-Sun Ch'u-Chiu's house. The former civil servant, now pig farmer Kung-Sun Ch'u-Chiu ('somewhat dazed' according to Judith Weir's stage directions, and well might he be) quickly puts one of his pigs into the black bag. When Tu-an-ku arrives, Kung-Sun Ch'u-Chiu tells him that the doctor has run off, leaving his black bag behind. Tu-an-ku, wrongly supposing that bag to contain the infant son of the now deceased Chao, repeatedly stabs the bag and hence, in error, kills the pig instead. This, of course, is accompanied by further cascades of ersatz blood on stage.

A Night at the Chinese Opera: Chao (Stephen Chaundy) finds his wife (Sarah Redgwick) is pregnant. Scottish Opera, 2008. Photo: Richard Campbell.

Tu-an-ku commends Kung-Sun Ch'u-Chiu for helping him to find and kill the orphan of Chao. But then the lusty cries of that very infant, clearly very much alive, are heard coming from the house. The no longer dazed, now quick-witted Kung-Sun Ch'u-Chiu explains that these are the cries of his own newborn son. He is very old, and he does not have a wife, but one cannot have everything in opera. Tu-an-ku, who is childless, asks if he can adopt the infant. Kung-Sun Ch'u-Chiu replies that it will be for him a great honour to have Tu-an-ku adopt his child. So Tu-an-ku, who has failed to spot the anomaly of the missing mother, mistakenly departs with the orphan baby of his formerly dread, now dead, rival, Chao, and unwittingly proceeds to bring up that child as his own.

The denouement of the play-within-a-play takes place twenty years later. The now elderly Dr Ch'êng Ying enters, according to the stage directions, 'furtively, perhaps bearded after his long absence'. He meets the now adult Orphan of Chao. The Doctor then proceeds, with the aid of a written scroll, to explain to the Orphan of Chao the truth of the whole affair. This takes quite a long time. The story is complex, as may well already have been noticed; the Doctor is not very lucid; and the Orphan is not by any means quick on the uptake. But eventually they get there. The now enlightened Orphan accordingly denounces his adoptive father Tu-an-ku, who, rather more quickly perceptive, exclaims: 'This bodes no good; I'd better get out of here'.

But Tu-an-ku is too late. Now exposed as a devious, murderous villain, he is sentenced by the Emperor to death by slow slicing. And the worthy Dr Ch'êng Ying is rewarded with the gift of a thousand acres of land.

There are not many truly commendable doctors in opera. Ch'êng Ying here must be numbered among that very elite few. He did of course have to wait twenty years for his fee. But even the most austere doctors are usually pleased to be well-recompensed, even if belatedly.

SEXUAL DEPRIVATION AS A CAUSE OF MENTAL DEPRESSION

MASSENET: CENDRILLON 1899
PROKOFIEV: THE LOVE FOR THREE ORANGES 1921
WOLF-FERRARI: L'AMORE MEDICO 1913

A dramatic device employed from time to time in opera is to start the performance by having the principal character, who can be either male or female, but invariably young, in a state of severe mental depression as a consequence, which is usually not at first recognised, of sexual deprivation. Sex hormones are surging through the patient's circulation, but to no achieved purpose. The plot, and the course of the opera thereafter, are hence concerned with the rectification of this highly unsatisfactory situation.

Examples of such a stratagem are to be observed with the opening of Massenet's *Cendrillon* of 1899, which is a version of the Cinderella story, and with Prokofiev's *The Love for Three Oranges* of 1921. In both of these operas the patient is a prince. In each work numerous physicians, sung by members of the chorus, examine the melancholy patient, fail to make any useful diagnosis, and depart, confused and baffled, uttering typically pretentious medical inanities. In those two operas the doctors have rather minor roles, as is shown by their being played just by members of the chorus.

The concept is expanded so as to become the pervading feature of the plot, and that of course is more interesting in the present context, in Wolf-Ferrari's opera of 1913, *L'amore medico* (usually rendered as *Dr Cupid* in the English-language version).

Ermanno Wolf-Ferrari composed this opera to a libretto by Golisciani, who based his text on the 1666 play *L'amour médecin* by Molière,[1] who had in turn plagiarised the Spanish writer Tirso da Molina. The influence of Molière is important. Molière, otherwise known by his real name Jean-Baptiste Poquelin, possessed elegant if sometimes cruel humour. He had perceptive insight into the psychological peculiarities of patients, as well as into the inadequacies and pretentions of physicians. The latter he regarded as pompous and usually futile.

Wolf-Ferrari's opera contains five doctors, all of whom, as shall be seen, have principal singing roles. Only four of the five are, however, genuine doctors; the fifth, who turns out to be the most effective diagnostically and therapeutically, is an impostor. So there are no surprises there. Had that fifth so-called doctor actually been entered in the Medical Register, his dalliance with the patient could have got him into trouble with the General Medical Council.

The plot is as follows. Arnolfo, a widower (baritone), keeps potential suitors away from his daughter Lucinda (soprano) because he wants her to care for him in his old age. In consequence, not surprisingly, Lucinda becomes depressed and anorexic. Lucinda's maid, Lisetta (mezzo-soprano), soon sees what is going on, and she decides to set matters to rights. Lisetta deceitfully persuades Arnolfo that his daughter has a physical illness; wholly tendentiously, Lisetta tells Arnolfo that she has seen Lucinda 'shaking in violent convulsions', which is quite untrue.

Four physicians are summoned. Professionally perhaps inappropriately, but dramatically aptly, they arrive simultaneously (a bass, two baritones, and a tenor). They enter solemnly and pompously, carrying canes, their symbols of office. They are seated. Pages serve chocolate, after which they each take snuff. Then, in due course, the patient is examined.

Tomes, the bass, diagnoses *sanguinis ebollitio* ('boiling blood'), which, in a metaphorical sense, is not so far from being correct. Tomes recommends that the patient be bled. Desfonandres, baritone, diagnoses 'gastric congestion'. He would prescribe 'an emetic draught'. Macroton, high baritone, finds that the patient is suffering from *morbus inflammatio vaporum fumigatum*, which I translate as flatulence, and he recommends a purgative. Both ends of the alimentary canal have thus now been addressed. Bahis, tenor, seems to be the most imaginative of the four (not of itself exactly an Olympian accomplishment). He announces that the patient has *humorum cerebri glutinorum* (possibly that means 'a sluggish cerebral circulation'). He would give her a tonic.

The four doctors dispute with one another, whereupon the maid, Lisetta, derides and mocks them. The doctors have been professionally careful not to make amorous advances towards the patient. The maid Lisetta, however, is fair game. Cunningly, their lustful approaches on Lisetta are partly veiled in medical procedures and terminology. Desfonandres feels Lisetta's pulse, and finds forceful agitated beating, signifying, and here I quote, 'an erotic heart'. Macroton admires Lisetta's 'beautiful clear eyes'. Bahis, peering over her shoulder with an eyeglass, declares she has *exorbitatio pectoris*. The fourth doctor, Tomes, is much taken with Lisetta's elegant ankles. It will be noted that between the four of them they have swiftly covered cardiology, ophthalmology, reproductive physiology, and orthopaedics.

Lisetta begins to experience strange tingling sensations. She thinks she can feel 'love's sting approaching', and she prudently decides to leave, the doctors, in great excitement, scrambling after her. The doctors collide with the father, Arnolfo, who is just entering, and calm down. One by one the doctors approach Arnolfo, confide in him that the other three are ignorant fools, proffer once more their arbitrary pretentious medical advice in cod Latin, solicit and collect their fees, and depart. Arnolfo is now a good deal poorer, but not much further forward.

Then the maid, Lisetta, tells her employer that she can obtain the services of another, and much cleverer, doctor of her acquaintance. This is the handsome tenor who has the remarkable name of Clitandro, and who has long been a distant admirer of Lucinda. Clitandro clearly has also bribed the maid Lisetta. He enters as a supposed doctor, dressed much more flamboyantly than his predecessors, and is introduced to Arnolfo as 'Dr Codignac'. The pseudonymous Dr Codignac insists on examining the patient alone. He tells Arnolfo that 'doctors may have to ask questions which it would not be proper for others to hear'. Arnolfo agrees and withdraws.

The so-called Dr Codignac's consultation with the patient is not too demanding. It quickly transpires that not only has he already been taken with Lucinda, but that she also has fallen for him. The fake Dr Codignac then informs the father Arnolfo that 'not all diseases are bodily – this one is in the mind', a diagnosis which is, of course, entirely accurate. He then artfully persuades Arnolfo that Lucinda can be cured only by going through a mock wedding ceremony with him. Arnolfo, foolishly, is taken in. Although he does not at first perceive what is going on, a real notary is brought in, a real wedding ceremony takes place, Lucinda is genuinely married to Clitandro and cured, and Arnolfo has been outwitted. Not for the first or, I suspect, the last time, a medical impostor has surpassed the qualified professionals.

---

1.   Molière. See Preface note 20, passim.

7

OBSTETRICS AND A RASH PROGNOSIS

DEBUSSY: PELLÉAS ET MÉLISANDE 1902

As was seen in Chapter 4, in Verdi's opera *La forza del destino*, it is nearly always sound practice to give a measured, careful prognosis. In this present work, unfortunately, the obstetrician (medical midwife) is rashly over-optimistic. Incidentally, midwifery has not been neglected operatically; David Bruce's chamber opera *Push!* of 2006, to a libretto by Anna Reynolds, has six main scenes, each centring on a woman in labour. In this book, childbirth features also in Chapter 5, and abortion occurs in each of chapters 12 and 15.

Claude Debussy composed his opera *Pélleas et Mélisande* to a libretto edited by himself from the play of that name by the Belgian writer Maeterlinck. The relevant episode occurs in the final act of the opera. Mélisande (soprano), the wife of Golaud (baritone), has just given birth to a healthy daughter. The mother, by contrast with the child, is clearly very unwell, and her husband Golaud fears that she may not live. His anxieties are not baseless. He had earlier assaulted his pregnant wife, suspecting, with good reason, that she had been conducting a liaison with his half-brother Pelléas. The obstetrician, a bass, anxious to reassure his patron Golaud, incautiously and in the event erroneously, predicts a favourable outcome: 'She will not die from this ... do not distress yourself ... who says we cannot save her?'

He should have known better. As he is uttering these confident words, the household servants file in silently, and kneel along the wall facing the bed with their heads bowed. This was, in medieval times, a sure portent of impending death. And at this point the sole candidate for such an early demise is Mélisande who indeed does, despite her doctor's confident assertions, die. Amid the general grief and gloom, his professional reputation has, sadly, been irretrievably lost.

TWO CARDIOLOGICAL OPERAS

Cardiology is the study of diseases of the heart. Hence a cardiologist is a specialist in such disorders, although the doctors who appear in these two operas would perhaps be more accurately described as general physicians with an interest in heart disease.

OFFENBACH: THE TALES OF HOFFMANN 1881

In this instance both the opera and the cardiac disorder depicted therein have been the subject of a serious medical article in the *American Journal of Cardiology*. The opera also features medical malpractice.

Ernst Theodor Amadeus Hoffmann, usually called simply E.T.A. Hoffmann, was born in Königsberg in 1776. He died in Berlin in 1822. Hoffmann was both a writer and a composer. He was also a painter of some distinction and a qualified lawyer, but those latter skills are of lesser relevance to the present account. Hoffmann was to become a central figure in the evolution of German Romanticism. He set down what were later established as crucial tenets of operatic composition, production, and performance. In Hoffmann's view opera, which is essentially the musical articulation of a drama, should convey the inner impulses of the story at every point; the music ought to comprise much more than a simple ornamentation of the verbal text. Hoffmann was thus carrying forward the notions formulated earlier by Gluck, and attention to those precepts was greatly to enhance the effectiveness of opera as a theatrical artform. The influence of Hoffmann upon first Weber and then Wagner is particularly evident, and has, understandably, been emphasized, especially by German commentators.

Hoffmann himself appears as the main character in Offenbach's *The Tales of Hoffmann*, an opera to a libretto by Barbier based on an 1851 play by Barbier and Carré. This was to be Offenbach's last opera; he died while it was in rehearsal for its first performance, which took place in Paris in 1881. In the opera, as the title indicates, Hoffmann, sung by a tenor, is depicted as a participant in various of his

The Tales of Hoffmann: Dr Miracle inciting Antonia to sing. The picture behind is of Antonia's dead mother. For the premiere at L'Opéra-Comique, Paris, the roles were taken by Alexandre Taskin and Adele Isaac. Illustration: Mary Evans Picture Library.

own stories, and pursuing a series of love affairs. In each episode, however, Hoffmann is frustrated by a sinister baritone villain. Often, but not invariably, dramatic continuity is established through the opera by having the same soprano and the same baritone play respectively the several amours and evildoers in the various acts. Offenbach died before deciding the order of the acts in performance; hence their numbering varies with different productions.

In one of these episodes, in which a cardiac problem is encountered, the villain is a doctor by the name of Dr Miracle; hence the audience will be aware from his first appearance that his ministrations are unlikely to turn out well. Antonia, nineteen years old, is the daughter of Crespel, bass, a violin-maker. Antonia's mother, a portrait of whom hangs on the wall, has died young of a heart complaint. Crespel blames inappropriate treatment advised by her physician, Dr Miracle, as being responsible for his wife's death. Antonia has inherited from her mother that same heart condition, and Crespel wishes Dr Miracle to have no involvement with the medical care of the daughter. Although Antonia has a beautiful voice, Crespel believes that singing will endanger her life, and he forbids it.

Hoffmann pays court to Antonia and, despite her father's injunction, she joins Hoffmann in a song. The father returns, and Hoffmann hides. Hoffmann then overhears an exchange between Crespel and Dr Miracle, in which the doctor claims, despite the fears of the father, that he alone can cure Antonia. Dr Miracle comments on the sinister red patches which appear on her cheeks when she sings.

He takes Antonia's pulse, and describes the fast, irregular beating; in the score, Offenbach has here set the accompaniment in triplets in duple rhythm. Hoffmann, by now greatly concerned, reinforces the advice to Antonia to give up singing.

However, after Hoffmann has left, Dr Miracle reappears, and urges Antonia to sing, conjuring up the ghost of her dead mother, a mezzo-soprano. Dr Miracle seizes a violin, and leads them in a frantic trio, which leaves Antonia exhausted. Antonia collapses to the floor. Crespel and Hoffmann rush desperately in, but the Doctor pronounces Antonia to be dead.

The nature of the heart complaint suffered by mother and daughter has attracted a good deal of medical interest and speculation over the years. Dr Leonard Dauber of New York in 1992 wrote an article in the *American Journal of Cardiology* in which he considered various possible diagnoses.[1] He thought that probably both Antonia and her mother suffered from a disorder called prolapse of the mitral valve of the heart, one of several varieties of that disease, this particular form inherited as an autosomal dominant condition, and frequently associated with a frail physique. Patients with this cardiac problem may complain of shortness of breath on exertion and they are readily fatigued. They can have rapid and often irregular beating of the heart, such disturbance of the heart rhythm being possibly provoked by increases in circulating adrenaline as can be caused by excitement of any kind. Sudden death can readily occur.

Antonia should, according to Dr Dauber, have been treated with a beta-adrenergic blocking drug (a beta-blocker) such as propranolol, which would have prevented the harmful effects of the raised blood levels of adrenaline on the heart, that excess adrenaline evoked in this instance by the excitement of singing. However, beta-blocking drugs were not available in Hoffmann's day, being developed by Sir James Black only in the 1960s. If Antonia had taken a beta-blocker she could have sung without restriction, although perhaps rather placidly. Her singing would then not have led to a rapid, irregular heart rhythm, and she would not have died suddenly. Against that, of course, we should have been deprived of a good story and a dramatic operatic portrayal.

BUSONI: ARLECCHINO 1917

The opera *Arlecchino* was composed by Ferruccio Busoni to his own libretto. This opera raises a question which has exercised medical men and medical advisers a good deal in recent years, namely whether an intoxicated physician should attempt cardiorespiratory resuscitation. The scenario usually set forth for debate is of a doctor on a long-distance aeroplane flight, a doctor who has just completed a meal accompanied by a fair quantity of wine, followed by at least a couple of brandies, then being at that point requested by the flight attendants to proceed to the aid of a fellow passenger who has apparently sustained a heart attack. After extended argument, no very clear advice emerged. The best that the *British Medical Journal* could offer was, I recall, that in these circumstances the physician concerned should exercise his own judgement. This seems a particularly obtuse injunction, since in such circumstances balanced judgement is the very faculty most likely to be impaired.

The doctor in *Arlecchino* is a bass, Dr Bombasto (subtlety of expression is not usually a feature of operatic nomenclature). He is a confirmed bachelor.

Dr Bombasto's great friend is the baritone, Abbate Cospicuo. The abbate is particularly grateful to the doctor for providing a steady stream of dying penitents for him to consign to eternity. The abbate, despite the celibacy required of him by his position in the Catholic Church, is, in contrast to the doctor, a notorious philanderer. Both are unrestrainedly bibulous.

The beginning of the opera finds the pair of them in the streets of their home town Bergamo in Northern Italy. They proceed to embark on a convivial evening, and enter a tavern. When, some time later, they emerge from that tavern, distinctly inebriated, they are confronted with a medical problem. A man is lying in the street outside, either dead or unconscious. Rather unwisely, and from a distance, Dr Bombasto pronounces the prospective patient to be dead: 'This man has died of a heart attack. It is what we doctors call *mors fulminans*'.

This confident diagnosis is promptly questioned by Columbina, a mezzo-soprano. She recognises the stricken man as Leandro (tenor), with whom she has recently been flirting, and she suspects, correctly, that what has in fact happened is that Leandro has been beaten up by Arlecchino, her jealous husband. Arlecchino has in the opera a speaking part. Unlike Dr Bombasto, Columbina examines the patient, and she elicits that he has a pulse and is breathing. Clearly, therefore, he has not died, either in fulminant or in any other fashion. Thus the doctor and the abbate have rather quickly to suspend their customary double act.

The next problem is to get the patient to hospital. The group of them go around knocking at the doors of the neighbouring houses, asking for assistance. However the townsfolk of Bergamo, like those of Glasgow, are well aware that anyone found lying in the street, and especially anyone lying in the street just outside a hostelry, is far more likely to be drunk than to be suffering any other complaint, and they prudently shut their ears and their windows.

Eventually, by chance, help does arrive in the form of a donkey-cart. As the abbate proclaims: 'The Good Lord has provided'. Clearly divine aid does not in this instance extend to motorised transport. And thus is the wounded Leandro conveyed to hospital. One can but hope that on arrival he will not be obliged to lie, in National Health Service fashion, on the donkey-cart in a corridor for several hours before receiving medical attention.

It has to be acknowledged that cardiological diagnosis and treatment do not show up well in this pair of operas. Dr Miracle is at best negligent, but more likely wilfully malicious. The inebriated Dr Bombasto is frankly incompetent.

---

1. Dauber, L.G., 'Death in Opera: A Case Study', *American Journal of Cardiology*, 1992; 70: 838–40.

9

SCOTTISH HIGHLAND GENERAL PRACTICE

JUDITH WEIR: THE VANISHING BRIDEGROOM 1990; PART 1 THE INHERITANCE

Only occasionally seen, and hence to be welcomed when they do appear, are operatic doctors who are professionally exemplary. One is the Scottish Highland general practitioner in *Part 1 The Inheritance* of Judith Weir's *The Vanishing Bridegroom* of 1990, which she composed to her own libretto after a tale told by Donald Macintyre, a cottar of Benbecula, to the writer J. F. Campbell of Islay, and set down in the latter's book of 1860, *Popular Tales of the West Highlands*.

An elderly highlander is sick and, despite the earnest attentions of his doctor, dying. This is, it must be emphasised, the Scottish Highlands and Islands in the middle of the 19th century; the doctor's therapeutic range is limited. The old man (tenor) calls his three sons to his bedside and tells them that he has saved up a considerable sum of money. At his death it is to be divided equally between the three of them. The father has no truck with banks or even banknotes; his financial hoard is of gold, hidden in the house, possibly in an old sock. However, when the father dies, no gold is to be found, despite a frantically thorough search. 'Perhaps', the three sons say, 'there never was any'. But the doctor (baritone) disagrees. His patient was not delirious. Also, he, the doctor, had known the father for forty years: 'He would never tell a lie'. And the doctor proceeds to elucidate the mystery by telling to the three sons a parable. This parable is of course enacted and sung in the opera.

The parable is as follows. A woman (soprano) is forbidden by her father (baritone) to marry her lover (tenor), that lover being in the opinion of the father too poor, and she is compelled instead to wed a richer man (baritone). But when the rich husband hears of her earlier lover, he, surprisingly magnanimously, sends her, together with substantial funds, back to that lover. This behaviour is quite unlike that of any highlander I have met; in my experience they are not at all disposed to send people around the countryside with large quantities of cash, although wife-swapping, so I am informed, is not unusual in those parts.

Yet when the wife arrives at the house of her earlier paramour he, on learning of her marriage, returns her once more to her rightful, if unloved, husband, again with the cash. This is even stranger, because that former lover was clearly impoverished. On her way back through a thick wood she is set upon and robbed, although one of the robbers (tenor) has a partial attack of conscience, and takes her (of course now minus the money) home to her rich husband. There the parable ends.

'Now', asks the doctor of the three sons, 'out of all the people in this parable, whose behaviour do you most admire?' The eldest son (baritone) chooses the rich husband. 'The forbidden lover', says the second son (tenor). Probably both of these sons are bemused by the weirdly unusual highland generosity shown by both the husband and the lover. And then, after a good deal of hesitation, the youngest son (tenor) opts for, 'The robbers who took the money'. That third opinion is, I think, the most realistic assessment. And yet, in so saying, the third son has, according to the doctor, incriminated himself. It turns out that it is indeed the youngest who has stolen his father's legacy.

The line of reasoning pursued there by the doctor does not seem entirely cogent, though he has arrived at the right answer. I doubt whether such evidence would be acceptable in a court of law today, but it clearly sufficed in the Scottish Highlands 150 years or so ago.

What is impressive nevertheless is the thorough understanding that general practitioner possessed of his patient. Nowadays, although the doctor would have more effective therapy at his disposal, continuity of care is likely to be distinctly fragmentary and insight into the patient's character probably much less clear. Indeed, some Scottish islands are now having difficulty in engaging a general practitioner at all, partly through the reluctance of doctors to be on call at night or at weekends. But perhaps even the most cynical of readers can accept the general practitioner of this opera as being a good doctor.

10

THREE OPHTHALMOLOGISTS

Real-life ophthalmologists, specialists in diseases of the eye, have suffered from a poor reputation in musical circles. Bach died in 1750 apparently from the consequences of a botched operation for cataract. The same quack ophthalmologist as dealt with Bach, John 'Chevalier' Taylor, failed also in 1758 to deal properly with Handel's cataracts. Even so, neither setback seems to have inhibited Taylor from boasting of his famous patients. Liszt was another composer who suffered from cataracts, and he was advised by his ophthalmologist, Dr Gräfe, to undergo operation. Although it was put about that Liszt was so fearful of the likely outcome that he repeatedly deferred surgery, this seems not to be correct. An unsuccessful cataract operation is believed to have hastened Glyndebourne founder John Christie's death in 1962.[1] At any rate, the operatic ophthalmologists who feature in the three works to be discussed in this chapter appear as impeccable, both ethically and surgically.

GYROWETZ: DER AUGENARZT 1811

Adalbert Gyrowetz composed this two-act Singspiel to a libretto by Johann Emanuel Veith. It received its first performance at the Kärntnertortheater, Vienna, in 1811.

The ophthalmologist Berg (tenor), a shy ex-army doctor, has fallen in love with Marie (soprano), daughter of Pastor Reinfeld (bass), but Berg's wooing is hindered by crafty rival Igel (tenor). Pastor Reinfeld has two blind wards, Phillip and Wilhelmine, both sopranos, but with the former a 'trousers' role. Phillip and Wilhelmine are in love with each other.

Berg operates successfully and restores the sight of the two. He then discovers that Wilhelmine is his own long-lost sister. Marie declares her love for Berg, Igel is discarded, and the two couples are united to general rejoicing.

Sadly, this once very popular opera has now disappeared from the repertoire. Gyrowetz outlived his stylistic period and his works came to be neglected even in his own time. He is reported as having said: 'What a peculiar feeling it is to remain alive and yet realise that one is already spiritually dead'.

TCHAIKOVSKY: IOLANTA 1892

Nowadays, fully informed consent must be given by the patient before any surgery can proceed. In the whole of opera I have found only one instance wherein this requirement has clearly been met, and that is by the ophthalmic surgeon in Tchaikovsky's *Iolanta* of 1892. *Iolanta* was the composer's tenth and last opera, to a libretto by his brother, Modeste. This opera is not, it should be emphasised, a comedy; the Tchaikovsky brothers intended it to be taken most seriously. However, at any rate for me, it is a work which conveys a number of evidently unintentionally comic aspects.

The Princess Iolanta has been born blind, but her disability has been kept from her; she knows nothing of vision or of its deficiency. Contemporary production photographs of Madame Medea Mei-Figner, the soprano who played the role of Iolanta at the St Petersburg premiere, do not convey the appearance of her being blind, but it must be remembered that this is an opera singer, anxious to obtain further engagements, and it would not do for people to think that she genuinely did suffer from defective vision.

The Princess has, despite her blindness, a boyfriend, one Count Vaudémont, tenor. Likewise photographs of the first Count Vaudémont, Nicolai Figner, in real life the husband of Medea Mei-Figner, the Iolanta, present a risible figure. Of course, in the opera Iolanta is blind without knowing it; thus it could be argued that she is doubly fortunate without being aware of her good luck. Against these notions the critic Harold Barnes has stated that Nicolai Figner cut a figure of romantic elegance which held audiences enthralled.[2]

Help is at hand for Iolanta. A Moorish ophthalmologist, of great repute, is found, one Ibn-Hakia (baritone). Nowadays, of course, Muslim doctors are commonplace in our hospitals. They excite little or no comment and are usually attired in the same style as is everyone else. This, however, was St Petersburg in 1892, and a Moorish ophthalmologist was meant to look Moorish; hence Ibn-Hakia's costume for the premiere was in that style.

Ibn-Hakia examines Iolanta and makes a clear, confident diagnosis. He affirms that he can operate and cure her, but he will undertake this only if she, as an adult, gives properly informed consent. This immediately creates problems, since she has of course been kept unaware of her disability. Her blindness is revealed to her accidentally when, in the garden, Count Vaudémont asks her to give him a red rose. She, having really no idea what he is on about, inadvertently gives him a white rose, and the secret is out. This apparent mishap does, nevertheless, have the incontrovertible benefit that her condition can now be explained to her. Thus she does give her consent to surgery, Ibn-Hakia does operate, and at last sight is bestowed. The very first object she ever sees is her lover Count Vaudémont, and she is overwhelmed with joy at the spectacle. There is general rejoicing, the opera ends, and the curtain falls. We can thence only speculate on what her attitude will be once she has had the opportunity to extend her visual repertoire. Perhaps Iolanta, like the audiences cited by Barnes, found Nicolai Figner as Count Vaudémont to be 'a figure of romantic elegance'.

VITALY KHODOSH: THE LETTER 2010

The Letter, composed by Vitaly Khodosh to a libretto by Bernard MacLaverty, was part of Scottish Opera's 2010 *Five:15 Operas Made in Scotland* programme (see Chapter 12 and *Dream Angus*). It is an opera especially notable in that the central character, Anna Semyonovna, sung by a mezzo-soprano, is a doctor, specifically an ophthalmologist. Female operatic doctors, as I have already mentioned, are rarities.

Vasily Grossman, upon whose novel *Life and Fate* the libretto is based, was of Jewish descent, born in 1905 in the Ukrainian town of Berdichev. In 1941 he became war correspondent for the Red Army newspaper Red Star, reporting, among many wartime events, on the defence of Stalingrad, the fall of Berlin, and the consequences of the Holocaust. He completed his great masterpiece *Life and Fate*, based on those experiences, in 1960, only to have the KGB confiscate the novel. However, with the help of Andrey Sakharov, a copy of the manuscript was microfilmed and smuggled to the West by a leading dissident writer, Vladimir Voinovich. An English translation was completed by Robert Chandler in 1985.

The operatic Anna Semyonovna is a fictional portrayal of Grossman's mother. Grossman always blamed himself for his failure to have his mother, then living in

The Letter: The ophthalmologist Anna Semyonovna (Arlene Rolph) discusses the efficacy of her therapy with the patient Shchukin (Dean Robinson). Scottish Opera, 2010. Photo: Tommy Ga-Ken Wan.

Berdichev, evacuated when the Germans invaded Ukraine in 1941. In September 1941 his mother was killed by the Germans along with nearly all the other 30,000 Jews who lived in Berdichev. The post-war official Soviet line was that all nationalities had suffered equally under Hitler. Admitting that Jews constituted the overwhelming majority of the dead would have entailed accepting that other Soviet nationalities, and especially Ukrainians, had been accomplices in the genocide. To this day a culture of silence persists in that former Soviet territory about the collaboration of some of the local population in the killing of Soviet Jews. There is widespread denial of any such massacres, and consequent extreme reluctance to help in the location of the burial pits.

The scenario of the opera is based on a letter written by Dr Anna Semyonovna to her distant son:

> ... My son ...
> This letter is to tell you of my last days
> When the Germans stormed into the town
> I knew I would never see you again ...
> I had forgotten I was a Jew
> I am a Jew.

As the Jews are being herded into the Old Town ghetto, Anna meets one of her former patients, Shchukin, a baritone. Professional formalities bizarrely persist despite the horrific events erupting all around. The doctor enquires about the success of her treatment for his ophthalmic problem. He politely assures her that his eyesight is greatly improved. Such strange courtesies and futile hopes continue within the ghetto. Another Jew, Mrs Sperling (soprano), optimistically announces to Anna:

> ... you could teach my boy French
> It would be such a help in later life.

The opera's grim tale concludes with Anna writing to her absent son:

> People carry on as if their whole life lies ahead.
> The ghetto is full of hope.
> The truth is I am about to die.
> But I know you are safe.
> ... it will help me to die, to know that you know.
> Knowing that you know – I'll die better.

1. Cataract. See Preface note 17, p. 308. See also O'Shea, J.G., 'Franz Liszt's eye disease', *Journal of the Royal Society of Medicine*, 1995; 88: 562–4; Norwich, J.J., *Fifty Years of Glyndebourne*, Jonathan Cape, London, 1985, p. 86.
2. N. Figner. See Preface note 10, Vol. 2, pp. 191–2.

11

WELSH RURAL GENERAL PRACTICE

SIR PETER MAXWELL DAVIES: THE DOCTOR OF MYDDFAI 1996
This opera was composed by Maxwell Davies to a libretto by David Pountney. The libretto is mainly in English, although Welsh appears from time to time. The action takes place, and this is emphatic, in the 'near future'; the 'near future' in 1996 would be, obviously, some time between then and now, and probably closer to 1996. The librettist and the composer intendedly created this opera as pointedly satirical; well-rooted in present fears, especially distrust of centralised, excessively bureaucratic, government.

There genuinely exists a village of Myddfai, near Llandovery in Carmarthenshire, Wales, a quaintly charming place with, most appropriately for the opera, an eerie ambience. There also really is a legend attaching to Myddfai; that is to say, the legend does genuinely exist, although whether that legend has any basis in truth is another matter. That legend is central to the scenario of the opera.

As the opera begins, the Doctor, a baritone, is recounting, as a bed-time story to his twelve-year-old daughter ('The Child'; soprano), the legend of Myddfai. She has of course heard this many times before, but she loves to hear it again. According to that legend, 'Once upon a time' (sometimes the events are more exactly set in the 13th century) a shepherd was with his flock beside a lake, 'Llyn y Fan Fach', which of course is still there, near Myddfai. A beautiful girl appeared in the lake, and he fell in love with her. After passing the test of distinguishing her from her two sisters, he was allowed to marry her, on the condition that if he struck her three times she would return to the depths of the lake, taking with her all the wealth she had brought him. During their life together he did strike her three times, whereupon she did return to the lake, but she bequeathed to him and to their descendants the gift of healing skills. Those descendants became the Doctors of Myddfai through the generations.

It does indeed seem that this same family continued to practice medicine at Myddfai without a break until at least the 18th century. One version of the legend says that the last of the line was a Dr John Jones, who died in 1739; although another account has the sequence continuing for a century longer, until the death of a Dr Rice Williams in 1842. The more recent provenance of the Doctors of Myddfai is, however, very vague. Those subsequent uncertainties give rise to some anomalies towards the end of the opera.

The healing powers of the Doctors of Myddfai were originally, and in the opera to some extent still are, based on the pharmacological properties of extracts of various plants and flowers, which are richly diverse in that region. Prince Charles purchased a house near Myddfai in order, so it is perhaps rather unkindly alleged, that he might find ready opportunity to engage in conversation with the profusion of local herbs. In the opera a list of these is evocatively chanted chorally from time to time: 'celandine, pimpernel, marigold, valerian', and so on.

As the Doctor is retelling this legend to his daughter (just the legend, not the gossip about Prince Charles), and we are of course now in the 1990s, he is constantly distracted by thoughts of a strange new disease which has broken out in his practice. Whenever anyone receives a blow while rain is falling, that person develops an horrific incurable bruise, spreading inexorably over the whole body. And as it rains a good deal in those parts, there is a lot of this mysterious illness about. The sick feel impelled to gather beside the lake, where they sing forlornly.

The Doctor can get no advice or indeed any information from official sources. There are no replies to his letters, and telephone calls are unanswered. E-mail is not mentioned in the libretto. In desperation the Doctor attends the governmental offices personally. The bureaucrats there are not pleased to see him. He has not made an appointment and he is severely reprimanded for trying to shake hands and for putting his arm on a chair, both actions which are 'officially forbidden as unhygienic'. His attempts to discuss the epidemic are fruitless; even the existence of Wales is denied.

It might be thought that such subordination of reality to regulation is a gross caricature, but such suppositions would be wrong. In 2010 there was an enquiry into the death of an Ayrshire woman who had, when taking a short cut across waste ground, accidentally fallen down a disused mine shaft. Her cries for help could be heard, but a trained potential rescuer, a member of the Fire Service, was forbidden by his superior officer to be lowered to her assistance because that would have contravened health and safety regulations. Apparently it was permissible for the equipment to be used to save other firemen, but not members of the general public. The victim was eventually brought out by a member of the Mountain Rescue Team, using it seems the same apparatus as the fireman, although willing, had not been allowed to employ. The Mountain Rescue man, being an unpaid volunteer, was not constrained by health and safety regulations. Unfortunately the victim died from hypothermia. That misfortune did not, however, deter the Fire Service chief from declaring the operation to have been a success, which predictably distressed the dead woman's family even more.[1]

The Doctor of Myddfai is told that he must obtain an official appointment with the relevant zonal health officer. The Doctor has of course no idea which of more than 800 zones is his. However, whatever his links to the original doctors of Myddfai may be, he seems not to be entirely bereft of magical powers. He is suddenly caught in a strange blue light, and music is heard which is suggestive of the supernatural. He makes an inspired guess: 'Zone 645'. The official promptly replies: 'Of course; 6th floor, room 45'. The Doctor is shown to that office, but there, once again, his accounts of the Myddfai epidemic are dismissed: 'You now submit a quantity of unauthenticated and unverified certificates which are illegal ...'

But then the Doctor hears a secretary in an adjacent room calling frantically for a doctor to attend the Ruler urgently. Calmly informing the secretary and the civil servants that he is a doctor, he enters the Ruler's study. However, the Ruler (bass), despite his importunate demands for a doctor to attend him, is in fact preoccupied with some ill-defined crisis, the nature of which is never in the opera clearly disclosed. There are several hints that it could be a war, although alternatively it might well be some other impending disaster. The date of the opera, 1996, is too late for worries about global freezing, which were by that time rapidly fading, although the converse concern, about global warming, was then getting well under way. Or it could be some other, once horrific, now largely forgotten, threat.

One possibility is mad cow disease and its sequelae if transmitted to man. Mad cow disease, bovine spongiform encephalopathy, or BSE, was a major issue in the 1990s, timing plausible for this opera. BSE was apparently a consequence of cattle being fed animal proteins. Films of one affected beast, staggering about crazily, were shown repeatedly on television month after month. Incidentally, and I always found this amusing, the British minister responsible for dealing with the crisis had the unfortunate name of Hogg. Fears arose that persons eating beef from such cattle could develop the supposedly related neurological disease, Creutzfeldt-Jakob Disease, CJD, and that whole swathes of the population would soon die. So far, fortunately, that human epidemic has not appeared, although worries have not wholly subsided; some epidemiologists have pointed out that the incubation period for CJD could be longer than was at first thought. One expert solemnly announced recently that the incubation time could be as long as eighty years. Reassuringly, if that is the case, the adverse impact will be limited.

Or, in the opera, the Ruler might in 1996 or thereabouts be worrying about the Millennium Bug. 'Millennium Bug' was of course the appellation bestowed by the media; no bacillus was involved. Many computers were not, it seems, programmed to go beyond 1999. The Millennium Bug would accordingly, at the stroke of midnight as the year 2000 dawned, cause computers to fail worldwide, with all manner of catastrophes, such as aeroplanes falling from the skies, submarines disappearing into the depths forever, power stations shutting down, and so forth. National Health Service officials predicted that failure of electronic equipment in Britain's hospitals would cause the deaths of between 600 and 1,600 patients. Again, happily, these disasters did not materialise. In Japan an alarm sounded at a nuclear power station two minutes after midnight. In Australia a number of bus ticket printing machines failed to operate. In the USA some slot machines ceased to work at Delaware race track. And that was about it.[2]

Of course, in the opera the Ruler does not know all this, and he is not going to be diverted from addressing these potential threats by the Doctor fretting about a real epidemic: 'I will not be ... deflected or delayed ... by rumours of disease from some unnecessary zone'. In angry desperation the Doctor strikes the Ruler. This really is very serious behaviour which could and should have him struck off the medical register. A doctor ought never, whatever the provocation, to hit a patient. But this one does. It is raining. The Ruler develops the dread Myddfai disease.

The second and concluding act finds the politicians and bureaucrats squabbling furiously but ineffectually about what is to them the worrying absence of the now sick Ruler. Their antics are alarmingly reminiscent of Prime Minister's Question Time. The Minister makes a statement:

> 'Our Ruler's ... condition is unknown, as he refuses to see any doctor except [here reading from notes] the Doctor of Myddfai. This man, if it is a man, cannot be traced, but it appears that he replaced his regular doctor on the 15th ...'
> 'Was the man vetted?'
> 'Risk category 2.'
> 'Yet he was admitted? It is quite clear that on several counts security is inadequate.'
> 'A strange doctor is admitted to our Ruler and then cannot be traced? On what is twenty billion spent?'
> 'This is a resigning matter for the minister.'
> '[It is] criminally irresponsible to allow this state of affairs to continue ... I have here a motion of no confidence bearing six signatures.'
> '[No – there are only] five – I have not signed.'
> 'We must produce a statement. Rumours are already ...'

The Doctor and the Ruler, the Ruler now heavily bandaged, enter. The Ruler demands to be taken to the lake at Myddfai to be cured.

When the Doctor and the Ruler arrive at the lake the sick people, hearing of the Doctor's presence, rush forward in a frenzy in their anxiety for a cure, and accidentally trample the Doctor to death. Then the twelve-year old Child, the now dead Doctor's daughter, steps forward. According to the old legend, it will be recalled, the post of Doctor of Myddfai was passed down the family line, from one generation to the next. However, that genealogical sequence was supposed to have ended, either with the death of Dr John Jones in 1739 or, in the other version, with the demise of Dr Rice Williams in 1842. The events now taking place on stage are supposed to be in the 1990s.

The anomalies do not end there. The Child is under age, and she has received no formal medical training. Of course, this is opera, and perhaps some dramatic licence is permissible. The Child is certainly well steeped in herbal lore, which forms the basis of the expertise of the Doctors of Myddfai. She recites the traditional incantation of the centuries-old herbal pharmacopeia: 'betany ... pimpernel ... valerian and foxglove', and so on, although the therapeutic relevance of some of the botanically derived drugs could, for the late 1990s, appear outdated. But not all of them are obsolete. Foxglove, for example, provides several varieties of digitalis, agents still used in the treatment of heart disease. The efficacy of the others is more questionable, and really depends on the credulousness or the gullibility of the recipient. Extracts of valerian are supposed to be sedative. Tincture of betany is rumoured to relieve facial pain. Pimpernel is said by some devotees to be a sovereign remedy for rheumatism. Pimpernel is also 'guaranteed to repel witches', which could come in useful, especially in Wales.

Even more surprisingly, the Child now also assumes political control, and her instructions are unquestioningly obeyed by the Ruler and by the civil servants. The Child orders the Ruler to walk into the lake. He does as he is told, and disappears for good below the water. This behaviour by a doctor is criminally unprofessional, and should, at the very least, merit her prompt deletion from the medical register (if indeed she is registered, which is perhaps improbable). The modern Doctors of Myddfai seem to be very dubious characters. One knocks his patients about; his successor orders their suicide. The opera closes with the Child, evidently now both Doctor and Ruler, asserting that any war is now over, and dictating instructions to compliant, subservient, official civil servants.

Despite the dramatic anomalies of that final scene, this is in my view a powerful opera, in which the political satire is even more savagely apt today than it was at the time of the premiere in 1996.

---

1. *The Herald*, 6 August 2010.
2. Booker, C. and North, R., *Scared to Death*. Continuum, London, 2007, pp. 128 and 161.

PSYCHIATRY THROUGH THE CENTURIES

Not surprisingly, psychiatry features a good deal in opera, and not just in connection with the tantrums of singers, conductors, producers and the like, although of course such antics can be very prevalent among those people. My concern here, however, is rather with psychiatry as we see it practised on the operatic stage. It is, I suppose, hardly surprising that psychiatry and psychiatrists should appeal to operatic librettists. The concluding scene of Stravinsky's *The Rake's Progress* of 1951 to a libretto by Auden and Kallman is set in Bedlam. Operatic producers have also in recent years found refuge in psychiatry; thus Harry Fehr for Scottish Opera in 2011 and Thomas Guthrie for English Touring Opera, also in 2011, relocated the action respectively of Handel's *Orlando* and Purcell's *The Fairy Queen* to mental hospitals. More specifically, several operatic libretti have engaged with psychiatrists and psychiatric issues presenting over the centuries.

PSYCHIATRY IN THE 11TH CENTURY
VERDI: MACBETH 1847/1865
Of the many doctors who appear in opera, he in Verdi's *Macbeth* deserves especial commendation. He is, so far as I am aware, the only operatic doctor to write down detailed contemporaneous case notes concerning the patient, despite that practice being emphasised over and again to medical students in their training as being crucially necessary. Verdi composed this opera, derived from Shakespeare's play, to a libretto by Piave and Maffei in 1847, then revised it modestly in 1865. (Ernest Bloch's *Macbeth* of 1910 omits the doctor.)

In the early stages of the opera, as in the original play, Lady Macbeth, soprano, is the dominant partner, urging her more hesitant husband, a baritone, to murder King Duncan and thence to acquire the throne of Scotland. Subsequently, however, she becomes progressively oppressed by guilt, and then deranged. She believes her hands to be indelibly stained by the blood of the assassinated king, and she walks in her sleep, ritually washing her hands in a futile attempt to cleanse them of that supposed blood.

Macbeth: 'This disease is beyond my practice.' The doctor (David Morrison), accompanied by a waiting-gentlewoman (Karen Murray), observes the sleepwalking Lady Macbeth (Kathleen Broderick). Scottish Opera, 2000. Photo: Bill Cooper.

Operatic somnabulism is in some ways perhaps more typically enacted in Bellini's *La Sonnambula* of 1831. In that opera the soprano heroine achieves dramatic effect by simultaneously sleepwalking and singing at a dangerous height – usually on the roof or castle battlements, while the chorus, more secure at ground level, utter anxious exclamations such as 'O orror!' and so forth.

Lady Macbeth's nocturnal perambulations remain earthbound throughout, but are no less dramatic for that. Her lady-in-waiting (mezzo-soprano) has engaged a doctor (bass) to observe the patient and to advise on treatment. As Shakespeare's text makes clear, that doctor starts out strongly, but unfortunately soon fades, as follows: 'I will set down what comes from her, to satisfy my remembrance the more strongly'. This is excellent medical procedure, setting him apart from, and above, nearly all other operatic doctors. But then, as circumstances progress, he comes to realise that he is getting out of his depth medically: 'This disease is beyond my practice'. Nevertheless, he still has to discharge two duties. He has been called out to the case, and hence must proffer some advice to the lady-in-waiting. He must then take his leave with as much dignity and grace as he can muster. In neither of these respects does he do well; indeed, in both he performs spectacularly badly. His advice comprises simply the injunction: 'Look after her'; his exit: 'So, good night'.

There can be few doctors who have not, in the course of their medical careers, occasionally found themselves in just such circumstances. Most, however, would hope to discharge their duties with more aplomb than the doctor does here.

PSYCHIATRY IN THE 17TH CENTURY
PENDERECKI: THE DEVILS OF LOUDUN 1969
A compelling account of therapeutic psychiatry as it was in the 17th century is to be found in the Polish composer Penderecki's opera *The Devils of Loudun* of 1969.

This is based on a true story dating from the 1630s which was recounted in detail in the book by Aldous Huxley.[1] The tale was then dramatized by John Whiting, and it is from John Whiting's play that Penderecki derived his libretto. Exorcism, as shall be seen, is not only of limited therapeutic value; it may lead to some distinctly adverse psychiatric consequences.

A central figure in the story and hence in the opera is Father Urbain Grandier, who has been appointed to the priesthood of St Peter's Church in the French town of Loudun. Father Grandier (baritone) is handsome, personable, articulate, a compelling preacher, and a womaniser. At first he is welcomed by the town worthies, but then several aspects of his rather arrogant behaviour, together with his amorous proclivities, turn that group against him. Initially one of Father Grandier's close friends is M. Trincant, the Public Prosecutor; but when Grandier gets one of Trincant's daughters, Philippe (soprano), pregnant, and then disowns responsibility, Trincant becomes Grandier's adversary. Trincant's room for manoeuvre is, unfortunately for him, subject to some self-imposed limitations. As he has passed off Philippe's illegitimate child as that of one of their servants, he cannot openly denounce Grandier as Philippe's seducer.

Another of Father Grandier's regular paramours is Ninon (contralto), a pretty, young widow. Ninon provides some welcome lubricious light relief in the opera, with she and Grandier from time to time getting into the bath tub together on stage.

The anti-Grandier cabal is joined by the local surgeon, Dr Mannoury, a baritone. Dr Mannoury, although by no means a model of medical rectitude, is not wholly devoid of probity. For example, when a journal of Grandier's movements is kept with a view to his denunciation, Dr Mannoury rejects that evidence as being flimsily circumstantial.

Grandier's downfall occurs when he is invited by Sister Jeanne of the Angels (soprano), Prioress of St Ursula's Convent, to be their Director and confessor to the order. Grandier regretfully declines, by letter. But very soon after that the Prioress begins to experience sexual fantasies centred on Grandier, whom she comes to believe has sent various devils as emissaries to possess her carnally. Sexual hysteria spreads rapidly from the Prioress to others in the convent, and before long three more of the Ursuline sisters are claiming to have engaged in sexual acts with demons sent especially for that purpose by Grandier. Dr Mannoury performs gynaecological examination and finds that all have been sexually active, although, as he promptly and correctly points out, that observation in no way proves that either Grandier or his demons have been responsible.

Father Barré (bass), the vicar of Chinon, and a reputed expert on exorcism, is sent for. Father Barré confirms that the nuns are bewitched, and he identifies several of the responsible spirits by name. Two of these, Leviathan and Beherit, are especially prominent and troublesome. Father Barré then embarks on a course of public exorcisms. It would be difficult even to think of an approach less suited to the treatment of hysteria. People from far and wide, including members of the nobility and even royalty, travel to witness these events, at which the various demons, speaking loudly through the voices of the afflicted sisters, and very conveniently in French, provide detailed accounts of their sexual exploits. All of these touristic exhibitions provide of course a most welcome supplementary revenue for the convent. Fortunately for the nuns, at least in this respect, none of the exorcisms is successful in actually expelling the evil spirits. When the exorcisms are for a time suspended, following an ordinance issued by the Archbishop, there occurs a most uncomfortable decline in the convent's income.

While the nuns do thus for the most part seemingly revel in the salacious publicity of all this, there occur some exceptions. On one occasion, for example, Father Barré diagnoses that the devil Asmodeus is situated deep in the bowel of the Prioress, and he orders the surgeon Mannoury to prepare a rectal enema in order to dislodge Asmodeus. This news alarms Sister Jeanne, who quickly attempts to retract her accusations. But she is too late; the enema is administered, to her loud screams of protest. According to the original stage directions by Penderecki, this enema procedure is to take place behind a discreet curtain, and out of view of the audience. As is well known of course, producers nowadays are often less restrained.

Eventually Grandier is arrested and brought to trial. At the trial Grandier confesses that he has sinned with women, but he emphasises that he is innocent of all the charges relating to St Ursula's Convent. Grandier is subjected to torture. The surgeon Mannoury is ordered to tear out his fingernails, but Mannoury refuses; that is not a job he says for a medical man. Despite torture, Grandier does not confess. Father Barré claims that the fact of there being no confession can mean only that the Devil has made Grandier quite insensible to pain. Again, Dr Mannoury asks pertinently what then can Grandier's screams have been about. Mannoury may not be one of the most commendable of medical men, but he is by no means wholly disreputable or, indeed, devoid of common sense.

Grandier is condemned to be executed by being burnt at the stake. Rather surprisingly, in a contemporary woodcut, devils are shown leaving Grandier as the flames begin to consume him. This I find odd in several respects. First, I should myself have supposed that devils would find fire to be rather congenial. Second, the devils, if they existed at all, surely infested the various nuns rather than Grandier himself. That woodcut, nevertheless, illustrates what a contemporary witness thought of the matter. Penderecki's opera ends at that point, with Grandier about to be burnt to a cinder, and the Prioress Jeanne shown in silent prayer.

However, the real-life historical course of events did not end there, but continued on in a most interesting fashion. The supposed demonic manifestations did not cease with Grandier's execution. Not long after, according to the Prioress, Isacaaron, the devil of concupiscence, appeared, and proceeded to take advantage of her chastity. (Rather surprisingly, she claimed still to be chaste at that stage.) And consequently, advantage having been taken of her chastity, she became pregnant. Perhaps fortunately the pregnancy aborted, the abortion being miraculously spontaneous according to her assertion.

Then another demon, Balaam, the devil of buffoonery, a spirit who had seemingly long dwelt inside the Prioress, announced that he was ready to depart, and he promised that when he took his leave he would write his name on the back of her left hand, where it should remain until her death. However, the prospect of thus being branded indelibly with the signature of the spirit of buffoonery did not greatly appeal to Sister Jeanne. She thought it would be very much better if Balaam could be constrained instead to write down the name of St Joseph. Inducing a devil to write down the name of a saint might seem to be asking rather a lot, but Sister Jeanne thought there was nothing to be lost by having a try. Hence she embarked on a course of nine consecutive daily communions in honour of St Joseph. Balaam did all that he could, and that very noisily, to disrupt the novena, but to no avail. To the accompaniment of shrieking and writhing by the Prioress, Balaam departed, and there, on the back of her left hand, was to be discerned the word 'Joseph'. To the name of St Joseph were later added those of Jesus, Mary, and of François de Sales. How or why François de Sales got in there I do not know. At one time I was disposed to think it was because François de Sales was the patron saint of writers, which he is. But I then discovered that he was not canonised until 1665, which is too late for these events. Possibly there was some kind of proleptic arrangement.

Bright red at their first appearance, these names tended to fade gradually over the course of a week or two, but were then miraculously renewed by some unspecified divine means. This process was repeated at irregular intervals from the winter of 1635 to St John's Day 1662, when the names disappeared completely, and for ever. All this was regarded as a holy manifestation and a sign of wonder by many, although there were a few querulous dissentients who repeatedly harped on about the problem of the inscriptions, instead of being evenly distributed over the backs of both hands, were all crowded on to the back of the left hand, where it would be easier for a right-handed person to set them down. The Prioress was of course right-handed. Some malcontents can never be placated.

PSYCHIATRY IN THE 20TH CENTURY
TIPPETT: THE KNOT GARDEN 1970

The psychiatric approach illustrated in Penderecki's opera, the exorcism of devils, obviously pursued with considerable enthusiasm in the 17th century, fairly clearly also had its limitations in the treatment of hysteria. I propose now to move on some three centuries and see if an alternative form of treatment, psychotherapy, has more to offer patients suffering from behavioural disabilities. The opera I shall consider here is Sir Michael Tippett's *The Knot Garden* of 1970, composed to his own libretto.

Psychoanalysis, a procedure pioneered in the early 20th century by Sigmund Freud and his one-time pupils and associates Jung and Adler (they later fell out), consists, as I understand it, in probing into a person's early psychological experiences in a search for explanations of subsequent emotions and behaviour.

The Knot Garden: Faber (Andrew Shore) and Thea (Jane Irwin) undergoing psychoanalysis by Mangus (Peter Savidge). Scottish Opera, 2005. Photo: Drew Farrell.

Psychotherapy very broadly comprises applying the results of such psychoanalysis towards the correction of psychological and behavioural aberrations. As neither psychoanalysis nor psychotherapy can be subjected to rigorous scientific testing, both have been, and are still, regarded with scepticism in some medical circles. Beyond argument nonetheless is that both procedures can be most effective methods of extracting money from the pockets of neurotic persons who have time and funds to spare. The composer himself underwent Jungian psychoanalysis, and one of the findings of that analysis was apparently that abuse and humiliation to which, as a pupil and boarder at Fettes School, Edinburgh, Tippett had been subjected, later had some adverse psychological consequences. Objectors have been quick to point out that such a conclusion could readily have been reached by the use of common sense, and without recourse to professional evaluation.

Even allowing for the exigencies of dramatic compression, the patients who have been assembled for psychotherapy in *The Knot Garden* are an extraordinarily disagreeable crew. There is Faber (baritone) and his wife Thea (mezzo-soprano), a pair in their late thirties or early forties. They are evidently childless; they are at odds with each other, and their marriage is breaking up. Faber buries himself in isolation in his work; Thea takes refuge in her gardening. From time to time, however, this rather dreary existence is enlivened by Thea emerging and beating up Faber with a horse-whip, a practice which he seems up to a point to enjoy. In the 2005 Scottish Opera production Thea dressed up in leathers for these occasions.

Faber and Thea have an adolescent ward, Flora (soprano). For there to be a female ward in opera almost invariably implies that such a person is the intended victim of sexual attention from the male guardian, and this opera is no exception. It has to be conceded that Flora repeatedly and very deliberately entices Faber, but as soon as he responds she takes fright.

Faber is something of an all-rounder. In addition to child molestation and masochism, with the appearance of a male homosexual, Dov (tenor), Faber begins to make approaches towards him also. Dov's homosexual partner, Mel (baritone), is black. Mel turns out to be bisexual, and he adds to the general jollity by making various unsubtle sexual advances towards several of the women. To this already over-rich psychiatric mélange is added the arrival of Thea's sister, Denise (soprano), a wounded and disfigured former freedom fighter. Denise is also a humourless exhibitionist and bore.

The psychiatrist, Mangus (baritone), has been engaged to deal with this remarkable array of psychiatric misfits with their numerous behavioural problems. Mangus is presumably due to receive a substantial private fee for his professional services. A doctor should of course give of his best whatever the circumstances. However, if Mangus is being asked to deal with this lot, in this situation, on the National Health Service, he has some reason to feel aggrieved.

This opera is notable as being the first to portray male homosexuality on stage (Tippett was himself homosexual). The date of the opera, 1970, is, in that respect, important.[2] Male homosexuality had been decriminalised in England and Wales, but not in Scotland or Northern Ireland, in 1967, an event which led the Reverend Ian Paisley to launch a campaign entitled 'Save Ulster from Sodomy'. Mary Whitehouse also apparently became involved. Those were the days. Homosexuality ceased to be an offence in Scotland only later, in 1980, and, despite, or perhaps because of, the efforts of Ian Paisley, in Northern Ireland in 1982.

Let us, however, return to the therapeutic problems of *The Knot Garden*. The psychiatrist Mangus addresses these by himself assuming the role of Prospero from Shakespeare's play *The Tempest*, and requiring the patients to enact scenes based on that play, those scenes supposedly relating to their several psychiatric disabilities. In the opera, at any rate, this process works surprisingly well, although not all participants emerge to their own satisfaction.

After that treatment, the married couple, Thea and Faber, are reconciled, and renew their commitment to each other. Mel, the black homosexual, leaves his former male partner, Dov, and takes up with the freedom fighter, Denise. The adolescent Flora is miraculously matured by the experience and she strides out boldly to meet her 'brave new world'. Tippett does really use those words 'brave new world', which are a quotation from *The Tempest*, in his libretto. And Dov, who is the gentler of the homosexual pair, is left alone, deserted, and sad. And anyone who believes that all that is destined to provide a definitive psychiatric solution to those problems is the sort of person who will believe anything.

PSYCHIATRY IN THE 21ST CENTURY
STEPHEN DEAZLEY: DREAM ANGUS 2008

This opera had its premiere in 2008 as part of Scottish Opera's initial *Five:15 Operas Made in Scotland* project, that venture comprising five 15-minute one-act operas by composers and writers in Scotland. The libretto was by Alexander McCall Smith and Ben Twist after the novel *Dream Angus, The Celtic God of Dreams*, by McCall Smith.

Angus is a popular, attractive figure of the Celtic mythology of Scotland and Ireland. According to legend, Angus visits by night, bestowing usually happy dreams. He may just occasionally be glimpsed skipping across the hills with his bag of dreams by his side. Angus, in the opera, is a tenor. The doctor in the opera is the baritone Duncan, a psychotherapist whose specialty is the study and, if possible, the therapeutic application of dreams. The patient is Olivia, a mezzo-soprano, distressed by the infidelity of her husband.

Olivia has a dream in which Angus and the Chorus invite her to a picnic, a very West of Scotland picnic, in the rain. Angus relates to Olivia another dream wherein the local inhabitants, enacted by the Chorus, have been changed into pigs. The pigs are persecuted by dogs, but are saved by the intervention of Angus, whom they then thank profoundly. This typically confused dream is interpreted by the psychotherapist as betokening the reconciliation of Olivia with her husband, albeit the rationale is left extremely vague. The opera ends with Olivia expressing her gratitude to the doctor, who then (presumably; this is not explicit) charges a substantial fee.

1. Huxley, A., *The Devils of Loudun*, Chatto & Windus, London, 1952.
2. Simeone, N., Scottish Opera programme book, 2005, pp. 13–17.

13

DOCTORS WHO FAIL TO EXAMINE THE PATIENT

PUCCINI: LA BOHÈME 1896
LEONCAVALLO: LA BOHÈME 1897

Both Puccini's and Leoncavallo's operas *La bohème* are based on Murger's novel *Scènes de la vie de bohème*, the former to a libretto by Giacosa and Illica, the latter to the composer's own text. The scenario on which both operas are based was almost certainly prepared by Leoncavallo and each composer was well aware of the concurrent activity of the other.

The heroine Mimì (soprano) is a Parisian seamstress suffering from tuberculosis of the lungs (consumption). She is befriended by a group of penniless artists, one of whom, Rodolfo, a poet, a tenor in Puccini's version, a baritone in that by Leoncavallo, has fallen in love with her.

In the final act, Mimì, dying and wishing to reaffirm her love for Rodolfo, arrives exhausted at the garret the impoverished artists share. In Puccini's opera Musetta (soprano), girlfriend of the painter Marcello (baritone), gives her earrings to Marcello and sends him off to sell them. With the proceeds he is to seek a doctor and medicine. Then Colline (bass), a philosopher, sadly removes his overcoat and departs to raise more funds by selling it. Marcello returns, having found a doctor who has promised to come. Marcello also brings medicine which has possibly, but not explicitly, been prescribed by the doctor. There has been criticism of that anonymous doctor who is thought by some possibly and perhaps culpably to have prescribed drugs for a patient he had never seen. Such judgement could be unduly harsh. There was at that time no effective treatment for tuberculosis, and the medicine was almost certainly a pharmacologically inert placebo, any action of which would be only psychological. Moreover, it is not entirely clear whether or not Marcello purchased the medicine on his own initiative. Colline then returns with the funds raised from the sale of his coat. Sadly Mimì dies before the doctor appears.

In Leoncavallo's account, Musetta gives her bracelet and ring to Schaunard (baritone), a musician, and asks him to fetch a doctor. In this version Colline is absent from the final scene, and hence is not required to part with his overcoat. Mimì dies before Schaunard's return.

In both operas the demise of Mimì is so quick that neither doctor is in my view blameworthy for failing to appear in time. I am also reluctant to hold Puccini's doctor negligent in prescribing for an unseen patient.

The possibly contentious question of whether in the 19th century a doctor's presence could benefit a patient with pulmonary tuberculosis is considered in Chapter 24.

PUCCINI: GIANNI SCHICCHI 1918

In neither Puccini's nor Leoncavallo's version of *La bohème* did a doctor turn up. Yet, as we shall now see, even when the doctor does appear, he does not necessarily examine, or even identify, the patient. The work is Puccini's *Gianni Schicchi* of 1918, to a libretto by Forzano, who derived his text from Dante's great poem *The Divine Comedy, Part I, The Inferno, Canto 30*. A doctor should always perform a thorough physical examination of the patient. In this instance he does not, with interesting consequences.

The action takes place in Florence in the year 1299. The elderly and wealthy Buoso Donati is dying. His relatives gather round, ostensibly to offer him their sympathy and comfort; in reality to attempt to ingratiate themselves with the old man in the hope of receiving as legacy a portion of what promises to be a substantial estate.

Buoso dies, and there follows a frantic search through the house for his will. The will is eventually discovered. Yet when it is read out, there follows disappointment, consternation and anger. Not one of them has been left anything; all is to go to the Church. They despair. Then someone has the bright idea of asking the advice of Gianni Schicchi, a baritone, the local general factotum and charlatan. Not all approve of this. Buoso's elderly cousin Zita, a contralto, in particular has a long-standing feud with Gianni Schicchi. Nevertheless, he is sent for, and arrives. Until matters are explained to him he cannot understand why, if Buoso has died, they are all looking so sad. Then eventually he is enlightened. At first he refuses to help. His mind is changed by his daughter Lauretta, soprano, who laments that if no money is forthcoming her fiancé, Rinuccio, a tenor, cannot afford to marry her, and she will perforce do away with herself. This is expressed in the famous aria 'O mio babbino caro'. Even persons who know nothing else of opera will be acquainted with the music of this aria. Few, however, understand the words. Not so long ago my wife and I were at a wedding where the bride and groom were so taken with the music that they had the song played at the ceremony. The words, which evidently they did not understand, are all about lifelong spinsterhood, despair, and suicide by drowning in the River Arno. They are quite unfitted to a wedding. But the bride and groom there were blissfully unaware of that.

In the opera, that aria does alter Gianni Schicchi's attitude, and he resolves to help. His scheme consists of Buoso's body being removed from the bed and bundled into a cupboard round the back. The idea is that Gianni Schicchi will then get into the bed, don Buoso's discarded nightcap and nightshirt, impersonate the now dead Buoso, and dictate to a new and unsuspecting lawyer, especially chosen because of his poor eyesight, a fraudulent will reallocating Buoso's money and possessions to the various assembled relatives.

However, no sooner has Gianni Schicchi got into bed and put on Buoso's rather grubby night garments, than the general practitioner, Dr Spinelloccio, a bass, arrives to see how his patient old Buoso is getting on. Panic ensues. Nevertheless, Gianni Schicchi rises to the occasion, imitates the voice of the now deceased Buoso, tells Dr Spinelloccio that he is feeling much better, but that he is too tired to be examined by the doctor. He tells the doctor to clear off and come back another time. Dr Spinelloccio foolishly accepts all this at face value and departs without examining his patient, boasting of the wonderful education he received at the medical school of Bologna (Italian operatic doctors in comedy all are by tradition trained at Bologna).

Thus the path is cleared for the entry of the lawyer and for Gianni Schicchi to dictate the bogus will. In the course of this Gianni Schicchi reserves virtually all the money and the best of the possessions for himself, leaving each of the relatives with the merest pittance. This greatly angers them, but as they have been parties to the fraud, there is little they can do about it.

For this malfeasance Gianni Schicchi was consigned by Dante to the Eighth Circle of the *Inferno*, along with other tricksters and the like. Dante, I suspect, was not a person possessed of much sense of humour.

14

FOUR PLASTIC
SURGEONS

SHOSTAKOVICH: THE NOSE 1930

The first of the four plastic surgeons I shall consider is to be found in the opera *The Nose* by Shostakovich, to a libretto by Yonin, Preiss, Zamyatin, and the composer himself after the story by Gogol. That original tale is allegorical. Gogol wrote it in 1836 in the reign of Tsar Nicholas I, when any criticism of those in authority had to be very circumspect. Explicit naming of those subject to dispraise was certainly inadvisable. So, Gogol's story, and hence Shostakovich's subsequent opera, are figurative or metaphorical.

In Tsarist Russia, and especially so in the first half of the 19th century, people were esteemed not for what they were but for what they appeared to be. That of course was true not just of Tsarist Russia but later also of Stalin's Soviet Union, as indeed of bureaucracies almost everywhere at any time. If someone has a recognisable docket or label they may be assigned a value, without the need of knowledge or judgement on the part of the putative (often self-appointed) assessor, a circumstance beloved of bureaucrats. The outward, superficial appearance is all. There is little wonder that *The Nose* was banned by Stalin, and not revived in the Soviet Union until long after his death.

The story of *The Nose* is simple and fantastic. A St Petersburg college official, Kovalyov (baritone), awakes to find that his nose has unaccountably disappeared from the front of his face. A nose is of course the ultimate symbol of status; lose it, and one is virtually invisible. The distraught Kovalyov frantically searches the city for his lost nose. There are wild speculations and almost as bizarre dramatic events. The Nose (tenor) is observed in various locations; walking about the streets, in a barber's shop, in the Cathedral, thrown into the River Neva, attempting to board a coach, in police custody, and so forth. As can readily be appreciated, this is an opera calling for considerable virtuosity in staging. There are eighty-five different singing roles. When the work was given at the Buxton Festival in July 2001 those parts were taken by just nine singers. It was said that

The Nose: The bereft Kovalyov (Jeremy Huw Williams) attempts to recapture his autonomous Nose. The Opera Group, 2001. Photo: Alastair Muir.

the events backstage, involving numerous rapid changes of costume, were almost as exciting as the opera proper as viewed from the auditorium.

After many adventures Kovalyov does recapture his lost Nose, and he then engages the services of a plastic surgeon (bass) to have it reattached. But the surgeon refuses, on the specious grounds that the Nose has been separated for too long, thus precluding proper healing. The surgeon has here a deceitful motive, in that he wishes to add the Nose to his museum collection of pathological specimens, a procedure which would now be forbidden in Britain's National Health Service. The surgeon attempts to reassure his distressed patient in the fatuous manner favoured by some doctors, pointing out that, devoid of a nose, Kovalyov will be less susceptible to colds. Hardly surprisingly, this advice does not console Kovalyov, who weeps profusely.

Then, even more perversely, the story reaches the press (inaccurately, it need hardly be said) and the detached Nose, rumoured now to have been seen out shopping, becomes a celebrity, while its owner, Kovalyov, remains a noseless nonentity.

Finally, as unpredictably and as unaccountably as it initially became separated, the Nose is spontaneously and firmly reunited with Kovalyov's face. His prestige and self-esteem are restored as rapidly and as substantially as they were lost, albeit his nose is no longer a notorious celebrity. But then, as he reflects philosophically, one cannot have everything.

LYELL CRESSWELL: THE PERFECT WOMAN 2008

The Perfect Woman was put on for the first time in 2008 by Scottish Opera as part of the initial *Five:15 Operas Made in Scotland* project (see Chapter 12 and *Dream Angus*) and was composed by Lyell Cresswell to a libretto by Ron Butlin after a story by Nathaniel Hawthorne. We shall encounter here an unexpected consequence of plastic surgery.

Contemporary plastic surgeons, at least according to popular public prejudice, come in two main varieties. First, there are idealistic plastic surgeons, who perform surgical operations and other technical procedures which are of almost immeasurable value; re-attaching severed limbs, correcting deformities, and mitigating the adverse aesthetic consequences of burns and other injuries. And then, it is held, there are those, mainly if not exclusively in private practice, who are supposed to, and almost certainly do, accumulate large sums of money by making ageing celebrities look like waxworks. Some very versatile plastic surgeons are even thought to pursue both courses.

The plastic surgeon we shall meet here, in the opera *The Perfect Woman*, is eager to display his professional skills before as wide an audience as possible. Bizarrely, the patient is his own wife, Rosanna. Rosanna (mezzo-soprano) has a red birthmark on her cheek. Although this mark has caused her humiliation, and led to her being bullied in her childhood and taunted at school, she has been told, and has consequently come to accept, the deformity as being the consequence of 'The Touch of the Hand of God'.

But now, her husband (baritone), the plastic surgeon, has developed what seems to be an electronic means of eliminating this disfiguring mark. In a manner remarkable even for the most extrovert of surgeons, he has invited a large number of medical and surgical colleagues and the press to witness the public elimination of that birthmark. The wife, Rosanna, who seems not to have been informed beforehand of the event, is led in, obviously to her reluctance. Her disfigurement is demonstrated to the audience. Even more oddly, the surgeon then requests the unrehearsed assistance of a member of that audience. A volunteer (tenor) duly steps up and joins the surgeon. This behaviour seems more suited to theatrical Christmas pantomime than to clinical surgery and raises questions not only concerning the surgeon's ethical conduct, but also as to how well he has established his technique. But he is confident. He now announces that he will make his wife Rosanna perfect.

By this stage Rosanna has, very reasonably in my opinion, become alarmed and querulous, and refuses to go ahead with the procedure. She has to be forcibly restrained and is handcuffed to the operating table. One might well wonder just how often plastic surgeons have physically to compel their patients to undergo their procedures by shackling them to the operating table. In spite of the patient's protests, she is wired up, the procedure goes ahead, and at first seems to have been completed successfully. But then, as the electrical leads are unfastened, and as the patient sits up rather groggily, it can be seen that the mark has only partly been effaced. The surgeon denies that he is to blame and angrily rebukes his assistant. I well remember such behaviour by prominent surgeons from my own student days.

The patient Rosanna has to be strapped down again, she is reconnected to the electrical apparatus, and the whole process is repeated. This time, however, the technique is fully successful. The mark has now gone, the skin has healed, and the surgeon proudly displays to the audience what he says is at last womanly perfection.

But the resentful Rosanna now decides to take charge of proceedings. As she points out, if she is now perfect she is also now the boss. She orders the surgeon, her husband, to kneel before her. He obeys. She handcuffs him, and as she leads him offstage gleefully announces:

> See ladies and gentlemen!
> The perfect woman ...
> And the perfect man!

The Perfect Woman: The plastic surgeon (Paul Keohone) displays Rosanna's (Lise Christensen) birthmark to the observers. Scottish Opera, 2008. Photo: Richard Campbell.

That was a glimpse of the manner in which at least some plastic surgeons are alleged to go about their affairs. I am sure that most plastic surgeons would deny that it was a faithful account. Either way, it is a tale which should warn surgeons against undue hubris.

DAVID SAWER: SKIN DEEP 2009

Skin Deep, composed by David Sawer to a libretto by Armando Iannucci, is concerned with cosmetic surgery and the quest for eternal youth. Incidentally, the surname Sawer does seem especially apt for the composer of an opera dealing with surgery. The plastic surgeon (he prefers to be called a cosmetic surgeon) is Dr Needlemeier, a baritone, who runs a very successful and prosperous private clinic in the Swiss Alps. A considerable part of Dr Needlemeier's work at the clinic comprises of course the usual activities of such establishments – the tightening of sagging facial and mammary skin, breast implantation, and liposuction. But Dr Needlemeier is no mere routine operator; for example his annual birthday gift to his wife Lania, a soprano, is to provide for her a whole new face.

Nor are Dr Needlemeier's skills restricted to the concealment of the physical tissue consequences of ageing. He and his clinic are dedicated also, according to his 'Mission Statement' as he calls it, to 'putting right what Nature got wrong'. In this connection Dr Needlemeier is persuaded to enhance the physical attributes of Robert, a baritone, who is the fiancé of Elsa, Needlemeier's daughter, a mezzo-soprano. These surgical adjustments to Robert's physique which include, as a special request from Elsa, genital enlargement, although technically skilled, are not a social success. Robert is so taken with his post-operative appearance that, Narcissus-like, he falls in love with his own reflection, and neglects Elsa.

Even more fundamentally, Doctor Needlemeier is proceeding with the development of an elixir of youth, which will, if his ambitions can be realised, actually keep his patients in genuine pristine condition, not just looking that way. In this undertaking Dr Needlemeier is of course following a long and well-established operatic line, which includes Freia with her golden apples in Wagner's *Das Rheingold*; the secret medical formula of Dr Makropulos in Janáček's *The Makropulos Case* (see Chapter 22); and the many operatic versions of the Faust legend, wherein Faust trades his soul to the Devil in exchange for prolonged youth.

Dr Needlemeier's approach to this problem is to prepare a secret broth or elixir, made up of a progressive accumulation of fragments of human tissue, all stolen surreptitiously from patients in the course of his surgical operations. Each of these specimens is, as acquired, added to the elixir in a metal container, which of course expands as the opera proceeds, eventually reaching the proportions of a city gas holder.

There is one very necessary, but extremely elusive, component of this elixir; Dr Needlemeier must have in it the testicle of a young man. Eventually Dr Needlemeier obtains this by thieving it from one of his patients, a Hollywood film star, Luke Pollock. The role of Luke Pollock is sung by a baritone (he is at any rate a baritone up to the time of the operation). The loss of his testicle understandably makes Pollock angry and depressed, and he spends the rest of the opera in an anxious search for the lost organ. I should myself have thought such a misfortune would have led a Hollywood star to sue, but the librettist here rather surprisingly had other ideas.

By the time we get to Act III, Needlemeier has moved from Switzerland and has set up a new clinic in California, where he is offering eternal youth to those rich enough to afford it. This Needlemeier Clinic USA is a gated community, in which the resident patients each receive their daily dose of the elixir of youth from the great vat. Eventually of course, the patients consume all of the magic potion. They have drained the vat and the elixir is exhausted. This is to the dismay of all except the still distraught Luke Pollock, because there, at the bottom of the now empty vat, is a small shrivelled object, his long-lost, now rediscovered, testicle. Pollock reunites himself with his organ by the simple expedient of stuffing it into his trousers. This is biologically and surgically impossible, of course, but we must remember that this is, after all, opera.

One might well consider that much of the action in that opera is implausible, but any such thoughts would almost certainly be wrong. I came across the following account, dated 28 December 2008, in what is called a 'fringe' medical journal, *Cosmetic Surgery News*:

> I've performed over 7000 liposuctions during the past decade [Dr Alan Bittner told reporters at his cosmetic surgery in Beverly Hills] and I've never had a single serious complication. However, I am left with a hell of a lot of fat, and I don't like to waste it, so I convert it into bio-diesel, or what I call 'lipodiesel'. One gallon of fat will produce a gallon of lipodiesel, and I've been using it for months to power my Ford Explorer. Despite the negative publicity, I can assure you that what I'm doing isn't macaber, and most of my patients are delighted that I'm using their fat for fuel because not only do they lose their chubby belly, they also get to take part in saving the Earth. [Dr Bittner was defending his actions after several patients filed a lawsuit against his practice, alleging unprofessional conduct.] Unfortunately there are people out there who are offended by the idea of using human fat to solve our energy problems, and religious extremists have been making threats against me and my family. I apologise for any offence given; none was intended. I merely meant to show that alternative energy is all around us, if we open our eyes and have a sense of curiosity. I would like to make clear that rumors about me having a private jet that runs on human fat are quite untrue. Due to frivolous lawsuits I have decided to close my practice in Beverly Hills and relocate. Probably to South America.

Reading that report reinforced my notion that Luke Pollock in the opera missed a trick by not suing Dr Needlemeier.

MARK-ANTHONY TURNAGE: ANNA NICOLE 2011

The opera *Anna Nicole* is based on the life of the small-town Texan girl Anna Nicole Smith, who acquired enormous breasts via silicone implantation, and in 1992 featured as a *Playboy* centrefold. In 1994, aged 26, she snared an 89-year-old billionaire husband. Unfortunately for her, when he died a year later his familiy successfully contested the inheritance and she herself died, drugged and alcoholic, in 2007.

In the opera, the plastic surgeon, a tenor called Dr Yes, unashamedly promotes himself as a 'cosmetic' operator, and brashly, certainly unethically, advertises his wares via slick talking and a catalogue in vivid colour. Anna Nicole, soprano, chooses size 'double-F'.

In Chapter 19 I criticise Tippett's operatic libretti as being substantially banal and confused. The librettist of *Anna Nicole*, Richard Thomas, cannot be indicted for confusion; the plot is too plodding and predictable to incur that risk. He has, however, attempted the evasion of banality by the unsparing provision of obscenities. This had the probably unintended, but unquestionably humorous, consequence that when the opera was broadcast from the Royal Opera House, Covent Garden, the BBC television surtitles contained (unnecessarily) numerous asterisks.

15

AN ALCOHOLIC FAMILY DOCTOR

BARBER: VANESSA 1958

The alcoholic family doctor is encountered in the opera *Vanessa*, which had its premiere performance at the Metropolitan Opera House, New York, in January 1958. The American composer of *Vanessa*, Samuel Barber, lived from 1910 to 1981. Gian-Carlo Menotti, Barber's librettist for *Vanessa*, and himself a composer of operas, was born in Italy in 1911. Menotti and Barber were for a long time devoted companions, who lived together in the USA for many years. In 1973 they sold their house in Mount Kisco, New York. Menotti then purchased Yester House, just south of Edinburgh. Menotti died early in 2007 at the age of 95, having earlier gifted the Scottish property to his adopted son.

The opera is set in Vanessa's opulent country house 'somewhere in Northern Europe' in the year 1905. Wherever in Northern Europe it is, the characters speak English. Vanessa, soprano, is described as 'a lady of great beauty in her late thirties'. Vanessa has shut herself up in the house for twenty years, shrouding the mirrors and her portrait, following the break-up of a passionate love affair she had conducted with a married man, Anatol. Vanessa's companions in the house are her elderly and formidable mother, the old Baroness, contralto, who has not spoken to her in those twenty years, and Erika, Vanessa's niece, mezzo-soprano, a young girl of nineteen or twenty.

As the opera begins, on a snowy night in early winter, Vanessa is excitedly awaiting the arrival of Anatol, whom she has not seen, of course, for twenty years. She and Erika make eager preparations to receive Anatol. The old Baroness retires for the night in her customary disapproving silence. The visitor arrives, and Vanessa is left alone with him. Not looking at him as he approaches her, she tells him to go away unless he still loves her. Yet when he replies she is appalled to discover that he is a stranger. Vanessa rushes from the room in great distress. The mystery visitor (tenor) explains that Vanessa's lover is dead; he is the son, also called Anatol. He persuades Erika to share the supper which has been prepared, and he takes her hand as the curtain falls on the first scene. The younger Anatol is, it transpires, a fast mover. We soon learn that he has seduced Erika, as a consequence of which she has become pregnant.

In the next scene we meet the Doctor. The Doctor is a bass-baritone; he is also apparently an alcoholic. The Doctor appears to be very close to the family, certainly a confidant, and evidently resident in the great house. We learn from the Doctor that he is dissatisfied with his calling; he would rather he were a poet. Surprisingly, he seems unaware – certainly he makes no reference to the matter – that several persons have, with at least reasonable success in one if not both spheres, combined those two vocations. John Keats, John McCrae, and Robert Bridges are three examples of doctor/poets. A fourth, George Crabbe, wrote the poem on which the opera *Peter Grimes* is based (see Chapter 2). Oliver Goldsmith could yet be another, although there is some doubt as to whether Goldsmith acquired a proper medical qualification; he certainly studied medicine at Edinburgh.[1] More seriously perhaps, there is the problem of this present doctor's alcoholism, an aspect which might very well impair his medical competence. Odd as it may seem to many, apparently not everyone is aware that intoxication can have deleterious effects on professional skill. Thus the *British Medical Journal*, whose editor never seems reluctant to risk embarrassment by stating the obvious, had a Dr Lee announce to readers of that journal in 2003 that 'consuming alcohol on duty can have adverse consequences'.[2] Dr Lee did go on to say that in issuing the warning he did not wish to be considered a killjoy. That was not the first thought that occurred to me about Dr Lee when I read his communication. However, in *Vanessa*, the Doctor overcomes the handicap imposed by his alcoholism when he is forced to confront a difficult medical situation.

Anatol, unaware of Erika's pregnancy, proposes marriage to her. Despite Erika being in love with Anatol, she senses that he does not love her, and she turns him down. So Anatol, clearly a young man on the make, proceeds instead to propose to Vanessa. Her attitude has now evidently softened, and she accepts him. A lavish party is given in the house on New Year's Eve. The official announcement of the engagement between Anatol and Vanessa is there to be made by the Doctor. As the time for his address approaches he is well into his cups. But he rallies and presses on. As the Doctor is proposing the health and happiness of the betrothed couple, Erika clutches her abdomen and faints. She partially recovers, then rushes out into the snow crying, 'His child! ... must not be born!' Erika then tries to kill herself by jumping into a ravine near the lake. This is certainly a lively New Year's Party, well up to Glasgow Hogmanay standard.

After a frantic search in the cold night, the unconscious Erika is discovered, her white dress stained with blood. She is borne back to the house, whereupon the Doctor, against all expectations, rapidly sobers up, and takes firm sensible control of proceedings. Erika is put to bed and all, with the sole exception of her grandmother, the old Baroness, are excluded by the Doctor. We learn, not surprisingly, that the pregnancy has miscarried. Under the Doctor's now shrewd care, Erika recovers.

Vanessa suspects what has happened, but the truth is kept from her. Anatol and Vanessa depart on their honeymoon, leaving Erika alone with the old Baroness. Erika now assumes the role played earlier by her aunt Vanessa for twenty years. Erika gives orders for the mirrors to be covered again, and for the house once more to be closed to visitors. She settles down to wait in her turn.

For the Doctor, however, the whole harrowing episode seems, although belatedly, to have been his revival, if not his making. He has achieved renewed professional confidence and self-esteem, and there is at least the prospect, if not the promise, of his abstinence from excessive and inappropriate drinking hereafter. Perhaps then we should modify the wording of that warning given by Dr Lee in the *British Medical Journal*: 'Consuming alcohol on duty can have adverse consequences'. To quote an aria from another, and very different, opera: 'It ain't necessarily so'.

1. Jones, A.H., 'Literature and medicine: physician-poets', *Lancet*, 1999; 349: 275–8.
2. Lee, M., *British Medical Journal*, 2003; 326: 165.

16

GENERAL
ANAESTHESIA

ROMEO AND JULIET (NUMEROUS)

General anaesthetics feature frequently, prominently, and very often tragically, in opera. As the stories on which those operas are based usually originated before the medical use of anaesthesia had become established, we find that in opera anaesthetics are almost invariably administered by amateurs with, equally consistently, dire results. The giving of a general anaesthetic is a delicate business, and should be undertaken only by a properly trained and qualified practitioner. In opera, for the reasons given, that is not usually possible.

Operas involving a general anaesthetic are nevertheless numerous. There are many operatic versions of the tale of Romeo and Juliet, which include those by Benda (1776), Dalayrac (1792), Steibelt (1793), Zingarelli (1796), Vaccai (1835), Leopold Damrosch (1862), Zandonai (1922), and Sutermeister (1940). Probably the two best-known survivors into the present-day repertoire are Bellini's *I Capuleti e i Montecchi* of 1830 to a libretto by Romani, and Gounod's *Roméo et Juliette* of 1867 to a libretto by Barbier and Carré. (Neither Delius' *A Village Romeo and Juliet* nor Bernstein's *West Side Story* has anaesthesia.) Anaesthesia does feature in Mercadante's *Il giuramento* of 1837 to a libretto by Rossi, and in Ponchielli's *La Gioconda* of 1876 to a libretto by Boito, both of these operas being based on the play *Angelo, Tyrant of Padua* by Victor Hugo. There could be added Glinka's *Ruslan and Lyudmila* of 1842, Wagner's *Die Walküre* of 1870, and Humperdinck's *Dornröschen* of 1902, in which are anaesthetised respectively Lyudmila, Brünnhilde, and the Sleeping Beauty. However, for simplicity the present account will deal just with the story of Romeo and Juliet, best known from Shakespeare's play, although originating earlier, probably in an Italian romance by Matteo Bandello.

Father Laurence, a priest or monk in holy orders, has secretly married Romeo with Juliet, these two lovers coming respectively from the warring families of Montague and Capulet. Romeo has been banished from Verona because of brawling; in the course of one such brawl he has murdered Tybalt, a member of

'Alack the day, she's dead, she's dead, she's dead!' The Nurse (Beatrix Lehmann) and Lady Capulet (Brenda Bruce) discover the anaesthetised Juliet (Estelle Kohler). Royal Shakespeare Company, 1973. Photo: Joe Cocks Studio Collection © Shakespeare Birthplace Trust.

the Capulet clan. Father Laurence decides that he will administer a general anaesthetic to Juliet, the intention being that she will consequently be removed from the malign influence of her family, later reawakened, and then reunited with her husband Romeo.

Although Father Laurence is only a part-time anaesthetist, and although the nature of the anaesthetic he intends to administer is not revealed, he evidently has a remarkable grasp of its pharmacological properties. For example, he informs the audience that a single dose of this un-named drug will render Juliet unconscious for 42 hours. The precision of that forecast should be noted; evidently the concept of biological variation has not yet occurred to Father Laurence. It has, however, to Juliet, who is fearful that she may wake too soon.

The anaesthetic is nevertheless duly given, and Juliet is discovered by her nurse, who in great alarm sends for Juliet's mother, Lady Capulet. The following passage now ensues (the words given here are Shakespeare's). Lady Capulet: 'Alack the day, she's dead, she's dead, she's dead!' From that pronouncement may reasonably be inferred that, at least in the opinion of her mother, Juliet is indeed dead.

However, the father, Capulet, more sceptical, now intervenes. Clearly he has previous experience of his wife jumping impulsively to unwarranted conclusions: 'Ha! Let me see her'. But he does no better: 'Out alas! She's cold; her blood is settled and her joints are stiff'.

At this juncture we may note that several aspects have medically gone awry. First, Juliet is cold; hypothermia has supervened. Hypothermia is, of course, sometimes deliberately induced as an adjunct to general anaesthesia in circumstances where a slowing of body metabolism would be helpful, notably with certain surgical procedures. But it is not entirely appropriate in this instance. Second, her blood is 'settled'. 'Settled' in Shakespeare's language and in this context means 'congealed'. Even the most ham-fisted anaesthetist would not be expected to cause the patient's blood to clot. Third, her joints are stiff. That also, obviously, is undesirable. One might further comment adversely on the lack of a proper airway, although it would have to be conceded that the presence here of an oro-pharyngeal breathing tube would rather give the game away.

And so Juliet, supposedly dead, is conveyed to her tomb where, later, she is discovered by her husband Romeo. Romeo is supposed to have been told what is going on, but the message has gone astray. Even so, someone should supervise a patient under general anaesthesia until such time as consciousness is regained. Had such a person been in attendance here that person could have informed Romeo of the true state of affairs. Unfortunately there is no such person, Romeo is not enlightened, and hence he, also wrongly supposing Juliet to be dead, commits suicide. He does this by drinking from a bottle of poison which he has providentially brought along with him against just such a contingency.

Then the 42 hours expire, the effect of the anaesthetic wears off, and Juliet wakes, only to find Romeo dead beside her. So Juliet, in despair, also commits suicide. In order to do this she is obliged to stab herself because Romeo, perhaps rather inconsiderately, has consumed the entire contents of the bottle of poison. This is a point upon which Juliet comments with a certain acerbity.

So now there are two corpses, gloom and misery pervade, the curtain descends, and the opera ends. Had the general anaesthetic been given here in a proper professional fashion both of those tragedies could have been avoided. But then, of course, there would not have been such a good story.

A SILENT GENERAL PRACTITIONER

RICHARD STRAUSS: DER ROSENKAVALIER 1911

Richard Strauss's *Der Rosenkavalier* of 1911, composed to a libretto by Hugo von Hofmannsthal, provides an opportunity which should be welcomed by any doctor in private practice – a minor ailment, an aristocratic patient, and a wealthy sponsor. Moreover, this operatic doctor is silent throughout. Silence in the medical profession is, of course, a quality which many persons regard as greatly to be cherished.

This is a well-known opera, familiar to many. In Act II, after the ceremony of the presentation of the rose, a dispute arises between Octavian (a mezzo-soprano 'trousers' role) and Baron Ochs (bass). They engage in a sword fight, and the Baron receives a minor wound to the arm. The wealthy host, Faninal (baritone), in great alarm, sends for a doctor to minister to his injured aristocratic guest.

How much is made of this little scene depends almost wholly on the imagination and creativity of the producer. With skilled direction and an accomplished actor as the doctor, it can come across as a most entertaining episode. There can of course be no doubt that in real life any private practitioner of initiative should be able to extract a very substantial fee from a situation such as this.

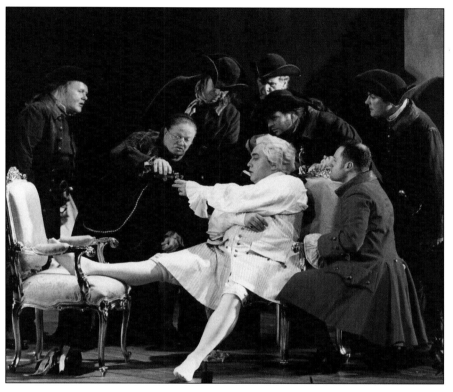

Der Rosenkavalier: A doctor (William Strachan) treats the wounded Baron Ochs (Manfred Hemm). Scottish Opera, 2002. Photo: Bill Cooper.

18

THREE QUACK DOCTORS

AUBER: LE PHILTRE 1831
DONIZETTI: L'ELISIR D'AMORE 1832

It is hardly surprising to find quack doctors appearing in opera. If indeed there is any surprise at all, it is that there are not more of them. One of the most successful of operatic quacks is to be seen in Donizetti's *L'elisir d'amore* (*The Elixir of Love*) of 1832. Donizetti composed this work to a libretto in Italian by Romani, who derived his text from that Scribe had earlier prepared in French for Auber's opera *Le philtre* of 1831.

The action of Donizetti's opera is set on a farm somewhere in Italy. Nemorino, tenor, a semi-literate farm worker, is in love with Adina, soprano, the as yet unmarried well-to-do farm owner, but she initially spurns Nemorino in favour of the dashing soldier, the baritone Sergeant Belcore. Nemorino has vaguely heard the story of Tristan and Isolde, and he understands from this that if he can somehow get hold of a love potion, and provided it is properly administered, he can induce Adina to fall for him. And then, there is for Nemorino a godsend. The village is visited by Dr Dulcamara, a quack doctor peddling fake medicines purporting to cure anything: haemorrhoids, headache, baldness, impotence, infertility, hyperfertility, or whatever.

Nemorino approaches the so-called 'Dr' Dulcamara and requests to purchase from him a love potion. Dr Dulcamara is momentarily taken aback; he has never been asked for a love potion before. Nevertheless, despite external appearances (he is usually sung by a portly bass), Dulcamara is quick on his feet, and he promptly provides for Nemorino to purchase what purports to be a love potion, but is in fact a bottle of cheap Bordeaux wine. That is what Romani's libretto says: 'Bordeaux wine'. There are several points of comment here. The date of the opera is 1832. The great classification of Bordeaux wines, centred on the Medoc, was introduced only later, in 1855. Since that classification, and probably largely because of it, Bordeaux wines have rarely looked back. Nowadays Bordeaux wines

L'elisir d'amore: Dr Dulcamara (Francesco Facini) proffers Nemorino (Edgaras Montvidas) a bottle of Elixir of Bordeaux. Scottish Opera, 2009. Photo: Richard Campbell.

include some of the most exclusive and expensive in the world. It might then be thought odd even in 1832 for a librettist to select a Bordeaux wine to palm off as a cheap fake medicine. And I think it is even odder for a Bordeaux wine of any sort to turn up in a remote Italian village. But this is, of course, an Italian opera with an Italian librettist. By taking a Bordeaux wine as a quack doctor's prop, the Italians are here I believe mocking French pretensions. Indeed, there is in my opinion evidence that this is the case. There was, as I mentioned, an earlier version of this opera, the French composer Auber's *Le philtre* of 1831 to a libretto by the French writer Scribe. Although the two stories are very similar, there are some interesting differences. The action of *Le philtre* takes place in a village on the banks of the River Adour, in the Basque region of south-west France. The quack is described as 'an Italian charlatan by the name of Dr Furbaroso'. In the only two scores of this opera that I have been able to find, there is no mention of wine of any sort; the nature of the elixir is not revealed. Hence I consider that in Donizetti's later opera the Italians are getting back at the French. If that is the case, the Italians have won this particular skirmish, because whereas Donizetti's opera has survived prominently in the repertoire to this day, Auber's *Le philtre* has disappeared almost without trace.

Nemorino buys the supposed love potion, and then proceeds to drink it himself. This is not, I think, the recommended procedure. Although I cannot claim to have gone in for a great deal of this sort of thing myself, my understanding of the matter is that it is the girl who must somehow be induced to swallow the elixir. She then gazes on her would-be suitor, seducer or whatever, and is lost. Nemorino of course does not know that. He is just doing what he has been told to do by Dr Dulcamara, and Dulcamara does not know either, he is simply making things up as he goes along. So Nemorino drinks the stuff. He gets slightly drunk, and makes rather a fool of himself, but not much else happens. Certainly Adina does not show the slightest sign of falling for him.

So Nemorino returns to Dr Dulcamara and asks if perhaps matters can be speeded up. He is particularly anxious because the wedding of Adina with Sergeant Belcore is now impending. Dulcamara is now of course on familiar ground; he has been through this sort of thing many times before. 'Ah, that is straightforward. You simply need a further dose.' This, however, raises a problem for Nemorino, because he has no more money. Nothing daunted, he raises the necessary funds by enlisting in the army via the offices of the conveniently adjacent Sergeant Belcore, and for this he receives a small fee. Nemorino now purchases another bottle of Bordeaux, as before believing it to be an elixir of love, and also, as before, drinks it himself.

This time round, things are very different. Not only Adina but virtually every other girl in the village is now chasing furiously after him. However, there is hereabouts another, possibly confounding, factor. Nemorino's rich uncle has died, leaving him a considerable fortune. Nemorino at first does not know this, but the village girls have got wind of it, and it could well be that the legacy, rather than the second bottle of wine, has done the trick.

In the end, almost everyone in the opera goes away happy. Nemorino gets the girl whom he has pursued all along. Adina has acquired a now wealthy, if somewhat dim, husband and she buys him out of the army. Sergeant Belcore rationalises matters by reflecting that Adina was probably not up to much anyway, and there are plenty of other girls around. Finally, Dr Dulcamara is especially content. Not only is he in the business of selling worthless medicines for the supposed relief of haemorrhoids, headache, impotence, and so forth. He now also purveys love potions which, as can be seen by all, spectacularly work.

STEPHEN DEAZLEY: DR FERRET'S BAD MEDICINE ROADSHOW 2011

This 50-minute one-act opera, with music by Stephen Deazley to a libretto by Martin Riley, was given its premiere performance by Scottish Opera's Connect Company of 14- to 21-year-olds at the Citizens Theatre Glasgow in 2011. The quack Dr Ferret (baritone) informs the audience how badly behaved children can be, but that they can be cured by his special elixir, Dr Ferret's Medicine for Bad Children.

Dr Ferret's Bad Medicine Roadshow: A female physician 'of the utmost fame' (Rachel Livingstone) and her male colleague (Ross McGregor) attend the sick Henry King. Scottish Opera Connect Company, 2011. Photo: Tommy Ga-Ken Wan.

Dr Ferret makes his pitch using children from four of Hilaire Belloc's *Cautionary Tales* as examples of bad behaviour. First up is Henry King, who made himself ill by eating too much string – a lesson for those who eat the wrong things. Of especial interest is that in this episode a rare appearance is made by a female operatic doctor. When:

> Physicians of the utmost fame
> Were called at once, but when they came
> They answered, as they took their fees,
> 'There is no cure for this disease'.

In the opera one of those famous (but here anonymous) physicians is sung by a mezzo-soprano.

19

A HOSPITAL INTERN

TIPPETT: THE ICE BREAK 1977

It is the unfortunate lot of many of us to be the recipient of bad advice concerning various matters, yet Sir Michael Tippett seems in this respect to have been especially unlucky early in his career. In the late 1930s Tippett was told by T.S. Eliot that he should write his own libretti. No doubt Eliot, who had been asked by Tippett to prepare for him a libretto for an oratorio, wished to avoid the task. Eliot was surely not so deluded as to believe that Tippett was genuinely competent in that skill. Tippett nevertheless evidently accepted the instructions at face value, and thereafter prepared his own texts for the oratorio *A Child of Our Time* and for the five operas of his maturity. His operatic libretti are in my opinion some of the most banal and confused in the field, one by no means lacking in numerous other dismal efforts. Those deficiencies in Tippett's libretti confer both disadvantages and benefits for those such as me concerned to elucidate the role of doctors in his operas. The participation of those medical men is often obscured by Tippett while, conversely, the interpreter can, because of the opacity of the texts, perhaps illicitly, certainly freely, extrapolate or even confabulate. These issues were confronted by me when I discussed Tippett's opera *The Knot Garden* (see Chapter 12). They occur also, albeit less pervasively, in another of his operas, *The Ice Break*.

The title of this opera embodies both actual and symbolic meanings. It refers in the former sense to 'the frightening but exhilarating sound of ice breaking on the great northern rivers', which signals the arrival of spring, an event described by Stravinsky as 'The violent Russian spring that seemed to begin in an hour and was like the whole earth cracking'.[1] The other, symbolic, musico-dramatic operatic breaking of the ice refers, according to Tippett, to 'whether or not we can be reborn from the stereotypes we live in'. The musical motif marking the ice break, which opens the opera and then recurs three times, consists of a brass and percussion chord with rhythmically manipulated minor and major thirds.

The action takes place (presumably, although this is not specified) in the USA. Lev (bass), a dissident Russian teacher, has been released into exile to join his wife

Nadia (soprano) who emigrated with their baby son Yuri many years earlier. Yuri (baritone), now a student, has difficulty in accepting the father he has never previously known. The tensions between Lev and Yuri are exacerbated by the surrounding racial strife in which Yuri becomes involved. Yuri then is seriously injured in a race riot. Luke (tenor), the doctor at the scene, prompts Lev, as his son is taken away by ambulance, to comfort Nadia.

Back in their apartment Nadia is dying. This remarkably swift decline is not explained medically. There are of course a number of operatic precedents for unexplained deaths. Several of Wagner's heroines, Elizabeth, Elsa, Isolde, and Kundry, all die inexplicably. Any doctor would experience problems in signing a death certificate for them. As an irreverent critic wrote: 'I don't need no dagger; I'll just die on me own'. However, Meiron Bowen does attempt, in the sleeve notes for the 1991 recording of *The Ice Break*, to explain Nadia's death by asserting that it 'denotes simply her withdrawal from the conflicts around her'. That pronouncement I consider to be both pathophysiologically and dramatically evasive. Yet Lev does seemingly comprehend those nebulous concepts, and reads to Nadia on her deathbed a passage from Goethe's *Wilhelm Meisters Wanderjahre*, wherein Wilhelm, now in a career as a country doctor, saves his son's life by bleeding him (at that time a regular, and reputedly effective, therapeutic measure). As Wilhelm then looks upon his convalescent sleeping son, he observes: 'You will always be brought forth again, glorious image of God, and likewise be maimed, wounded afresh from within or without'. That passage supposedly hints at a reconciliation between Lev and Yuri.

In his consulting room at the hospital, the doctor, Luke, tells Lev that Yuri will recover, and that he, Lev, now a widower, must accept responsibility for Yuri. In the operating theatre, Yuri bursts both actually and symbolically from his plaster cast. He is wheeled out to meet his father, and the opera ends with Lev again quoting Goethe's statement that the cycle of conflict and reconciliation is an eternal feature of human existence.

Although in this opera the doctor has a pivotal dramatic role, his contributions are brief, and he is a character never adequately developed by Tippett. The several medical situations, although critical to the evolution of the drama, are improbable and are superficially portrayed. In the original Covent Garden production by Sam Wanamaker, the presentation was moreover not facilitated by evident naiveté concerning medical procedures. At one point Yuri appeared to be receiving an intravenous infusion into his big toe. There would be no harm, and much potential benefit, if operatic librettists and producers were to receive brief medical and surgical instruction.

---

1. Quotations from booklet accompanying EMI recording 7243 5 86585 2 1.

20

TWO RESEARCH DOCTORS

BERG: WOZZECK 1925
GURLITT: WOZZECK 1926

I shall consider here two operas based on a play written by a medical man, both of which present as one of the characters an especially unpleasant doctor who is engaged in medical research.

Karl Georg Büchner was born in Darmstadt in 1813, the year of birth also of the composers Wagner and Verdi. He received his medical education at the universities of Strasbourg and Giessen. In the course of his brief, but very productive life, Büchner wrote three plays, one novel, at least one inflammatory left-wing revolutionary tract, and a treatise on the comparative anatomy of the cranial nerves. That latter dissertation was of sufficient scientific distinction as to lead to his appointment to the faculty at the University of Zurich. It was a position which, however, he was to enjoy only briefly, as he died during an epidemic of typhus in that city in 1837.

The operas to be discussed here are the two entitled *Wozzeck*. Of these the first, and by far the better known, is that by Alban Berg, completed in 1922 to the composer's own libretto which he had simply edited from Büchner's play *Woyzeck*. This play was left in poorly legible handwritten form at Büchner's death, and the obscure legibility explains why the play and the opera have come down to us with slightly different titles. *Woyzeck* is apparently the correct form, but was initially misread as *Wozzeck*. Both the play and Berg's opera enjoy sustained popularity; both have been staged in Scotland successfully in recent years. Manfred Gurlitt's *Wozzeck* appeared four months after that by Berg, and has remained in its shadow ever since. Nevertheless its premiere in Bremen on 22 April 1926 attracted much attention at the time. The following account is based mainly on Berg's opera; I have never seen a performance of Gurlitt's *Wozzeck*.

The story features a research physician ('The Doctor', bass), a rather unpleasant character, apparently based on one of Büchner's teachers at medical school – a teacher whom he evidently held in poor esteem. Nowadays, before any research

Wozzeck: The Doctor (Roderick Kennedy) experiments on Wozzeck (Benjamin Luxon). Scottish Opera, 1983. Photo: Eric Thorburn.

procedure can be undertaken on patients or volunteers, approval has to be granted by an independent ethical supervisory committee, that phrase being, in medical parlance, frequently elided, without a trace of conscious humour, to 'ethical committee'. Such approval was not required in either Büchner's day or in the 1920s, and is certainly not sought by the Doctor in *Wozzeck*.

The eponymous hero Wozzeck (baritone) is an impecunious private soldier, supposedly simple, yet, despite even his own low self-esteem, a person capable of profound philosophical insights. Büchner was very much an apologist for the proletariat, and that idealism is expressed here through the tribulations of poor Wozzeck. Wozzeck ekes out his meagre military pay by taking part as a subject for the Doctor's experiments. Unfortunately for him, Wozzeck is discovered by the Doctor perpetrating modest fraud in the course of those studies. Wozzeck has been placed on a fixed diet and is meant to provide complete 24-hour urine collections so that the dietary metabolites in the urine can be measured. These urine saves are incomplete. The Doctor knows they are incomplete because he has by chance observed Wozzeck passing urine in the street. Surprisingly, Alban Berg was obliged to bowdlerise his libretto before the opera's premiere in 1925 in Berlin. Mention on stage of the passing of urine was held to be too indelicate for the susceptibility of the Berliners, to me surprisingly so, because I had previously understood that anything went in the Berlin theatre in those days. Thus the Doctor is required to sing, 'I saw you coughing in the street', a phrase which makes neither dramatic nor physiological sense. Probably in the present more permissive era we should return to Büchner's original 'urinating in the street'.

The Doctor in some productions performs on Wozzeck rather ill-defined but evidently unpleasant electrophysiological experiments. Dramatically this sequence is most effective when presented in a restrained fashion, yet few directors can resist the temptation to over-elaborate hereabouts, often to inappropriately risible effect. The import nonetheless is unambiguous. Doctors generally and research physicians in particular are to be seen as disreputable egotists coercing and maltreating their experimental subjects.

Wozzeck goes on to be patronised and insulted by his Captain (tenor), and then to be beaten up by the Drum Major (heldentenor). The Drum Major entices and seduces Wozzeck's common-law wife Marie (soprano). Wozzeck murders Marie in a fit of jealousy and then commits suicide. The final scene shows their illegitimate child playing happily unaware of the deaths of his parents. Sometimes, mistakenly, an extra scene from the play, a scene which the composer Berg had excised, is inserted to conclude the opera, wherein Wozzeck's body, lying on a slab in the post-mortem room, is dissected enthusiastically by the Doctor. I think that Berg was correct; that scene should be omitted from the opera.

In *Wozzeck* Berg combined text and music to superb dramatic effect. This is certainly one of the artistic pinnacles of the 20th century. Some commentators hold that it is the greatest opera of all time.

SALLY BEAMISH: MONSTER 2002
GREG SANDOW FRANKENSTEIN 2003

Monster is an opera which was commissioned jointly by Scottish Opera and the Brighton Festival. It had its premiere performance at Scottish Opera's Theatre Royal Glasgow on 28 February 2002. This was to be the first opera by the distinguished Scottish-based composer Sally Beamish, to a libretto by the similarly prominent Scottish writer Janice Galloway. Composers who have achieved a successful opera at their first attempt are rare; the list of those who have failed at that first attempt is lengthy and impressive. It includes Wagner; probably also Verdi; certainly Puccini, Richard Strauss and Janáček. Britten's *Paul Bunyan* was initially poorly received. Beethoven struggled for years with *Fidelio*; his first attempt flopped at the premiere in 1805, and that version is now hardly ever performed. Mozart's first opera, *Apollo and Hyacinth*, is not one of his finest efforts, although as Mozart was only eleven years old when he composed it, we should perhaps temper our criticism in that instance.

It is therefore not I think unreasonable, Mozart notwithstanding, to suggest that composers who are essaying their first opera, and their librettists, should be wary. Several precepts can, with some cautious confidence, be set out for their consideration. First, there should be plenty of physical action which can be

Monster: Dr Victor Frankpierre/Frankenstein (Stephen Allen). Scottish Opera, 2002. Photo: Drew Farrell.

portrayed musically on stage. There are very few operas which have dealt successfully with abstract concepts; *Capriccio*, by Richard Strauss, which reflects on the comparative operatic priority of words and music, is a rare exception to that rule. Second, that physical action should be focused, not rambling or diffuse. Third, the opera should not contain an excessive number of characters. This is in any case an important commercial consideration for opera companies, which are routinely in straitened financial circumstances. More importantly, from the dramatic aspect, limiting the number of performers concentrates and clarifies the stage action. Those are, I think, prudent injunctions. They can be over-ridden but only with good reason, and even then, only after due consideration.

Let us then, with those thoughts, consider the opera *Monster*. Beamish and Galloway decided to base this on Mary Shelley's novel *Frankenstein, The Modern Prometheus*, published in 1818. There is plenty of physical action in that novel. Dr Victor Frankenstein is held by some to be a real historical figure, a native of

Geneva. When we meet him in Mary Shelley's book (and Dr Frankpierre, his counterpart in the opera), he is working in the Department of Medicine in the University of Ingolstadt, a town on the River Danube. Others have suggested that the character Dr Frankenstein is based on a Dr James Lind of Windsor,[1] a person who certainly did exist, and was well known to Percy Bysshe Shelley. Dr Frankenstein has been impressed by the physiological experiments of the Italian physician Luigi Galvani, who demonstrated that violent muscular twitchings could be induced in dead frogs by electrical stimulation of their nerves. Dr Frankenstein believes that he can employ similar methods to impart life into inanimate matter. He collects bones and sundry other human tissues from charnel houses, constructs the semblance of a man and, apparently by using the electrical procedures of Galvani, succeeds in bringing the creature to life.

But then unforeseen difficulties arise. Frankenstein's monster is possessed of supernatural strength and is terrible in appearance. Its awful aspect evokes fear and loathing, even in Dr Frankenstein, despite his pride in his scientific achievement. Nevertheless the monster becomes culturally educated by studies of Plutarch, Milton, and Goethe, among others (the creature is impressively multilingual), and develops human emotions. Not surprisingly, the monster then becomes lonely and miserable, and begs Frankenstein to create for it a female mate. Dr Frankenstein is however so horrified at the monster's awful appearance and the prospect of a race of such beings, that he refuses to do this, whereupon the monster, in great resentment, turns against his creator. The monster kills Dr Frankenstein's young brother, William; his friend Clerval; and Frankenstein's wife Elizabeth. Not before time, Dr Frankenstein decides he must destroy the monster he has created. He pursues it along the River Rhône, through the Alps, by the Mediterranean Sea, via Russia and Tartary, and eventually to the Arctic, where, however, the monster apparently kills him, Frankenstein, before it commits suicide.

There, it might be supposed, is plenty of action, fertile material for an operatic libretto. Thomas Disch, the librettist of Greg Sandow's opera *Frankenstein*, completed in 1981 and performed in part by New York City Opera in 2003, based his text on that story. However, the librettist of Beamish's opera, Janice Galloway, saw things differently. She, ambitiously and daringly, decided to deal not with the adventures of the monster as they were described in Mary Shelley's novel, but rather with the circumstances leading up to the writing of the novel, an approach more intellectual, as one might perhaps expect of a prominent writer, but perilously abstract. We thus meet, in the opera, a very large number and a wide range of characters, but with one exception, they are not those of the novel.

There is Mary Shelley's mother, Mary Wollstonecraft, famous herself as a pioneer of women's rights. Mary Wollstonecraft had died at her daughter's birth, but that did not deter the composer and librettist from inserting her into the opera. They cast the mother, Mary Wollstonecraft, as a contralto, and have her spirit step out of her portrait from time to time and join in the proceedings, a stratagem which had earlier been employed in Offenbach's *The Tales of Hoffmann* (see Chapter 8).

Mary Shelley's father, William Godwin, baritone in the opera, has earlier been a champion of free love, but his principles desert him when his daughter Mary takes up with the already married poet Percy Bysshe Shelley, whereupon Godwin disowns his daughter. Other characters include Jane Clairmont (mezzo-soprano), Mary Shelley's step-sister; also Charles Lamb (tenor) and his sister Mary Lamb (mezzo-soprano), writers and literary critics; and two more poets, Samuel Taylor Coleridge (bass) and Lord Byron (baritone).

There are two doctors in the opera. There is Lord Byron's personal physician, Dr Polidori (tenor). In the opera Dr Polidori engages in no medical work, apart from advocating more sleep for all; a largely uncontroversial piece of advice. Otherwise his sole involvement is to be repeatedly insulted by his patron, Lord Byron (see also Chapter 37). And then, of course, we have Dr Frankenstein, whose medical and scientific achievements were outlined above. In the opera he (or at any rate his alter ego) goes by the French version of his name, Frankpierre, and he is sung by yet another tenor.

The climax of the opera occurs with Mary Shelley, together with her partner, Percy Bysshe Shelley, later to become her husband, spending the summer of 1816 at the Villa Diodati, Geneva, together with Lord Byron and others. They are confined to the house by severe prolonged storms (these genuinely did occur in that year and were apparently a consequence of an eruption of the volcano Mount Tambora), and they decide to pass the time by each writing a tale of the supernatural.

The story of the monster is Mary Shelley's effort, inspired either by her acquaintance with a real Dr Frankenstein or by Percy Shelley's with Dr Lind. The experiment of Professor Jeffrey of Glasgow, who applied galvanic stimuli to the corpse of an executed criminal, took place in 1818, and is therefore too late to have influenced Mary Shelley. The opera concludes at the point where Mary Shelley has just conceived the plot of her novel, and we never, in the opera, despite its title, encounter the monster. At the very end there is just the briefest glimpse of its projected image. This monster appeared at the Glasgow premiere to be a good deal more presentable than Mary Shelley specified in her novel.

In the opera then, composer and librettist displayed brave intellectual disregard of the recommended tenets of operatic construction. Critical opinion was divided on whether their lofty literary and hence musico-dramatic approach was successful. One commentator, Barry Millington, thought the work promised to be a success:[2] another, Rodney Milnes, did not.[3] Others who saw the opera no doubt formed their own views on the issue.

---

1. Goulding, C., 'The Real Doctor Frankenstein?', *Journal of The Royal Society of Medicine* 2002; 95: 257–9.
2. Millington, B., *Opera*, 2002; 53: 173–7.
3. Milnes, R., *Opera*, 2002; 53: 855.

21

A FRAUDULENT GENERAL PRACTITIONER

DONIZETTI: DON PASQUALE 1843

The opera *Don Pasquale* is derived from Ben Jonson's much-admired play *Epicene* or *The Silent Woman*, a play which, like Shakespeare's *Romeo and Juliet* and *The Merry Wives of Windsor*, has more than once been taken up as the basis for an operatic libretto. Another derivative is Richard Strauss's *Die Schweigsame Frau* of 1935. However, in Jonson's original play and in the Richard Strauss opera the tergiversating dissembler is a barber. In the Donizetti version, regrettably, he is a doctor. A doctor ought not of course to defraud his patients. Here, reprehensibly, albeit amusingly, he does.

Donizetti's opera *Don Pasquale*, to a libretto by Ruffini and the composer himself, has four principal characters. They are the seductive Norina, soprano; her beloved Ernesto, tenor; Ernesto's uncle Don Pasquale, bass, an elderly, wealthy bachelor; and Dr Malatesta, a suave, manipulative baritone, general practitioner to Don Pasquale. 'Malatesta' can be broadly translated as 'headache'; subtlety of nomenclature is not usually a feature of Donizetti comedies.

The ageing, curmudgeonly Don Pasquale has decided to disinherit his nephew Ernesto, who has refused to marry the woman Don Pasquale has chosen for him. This refusal is understandable, because of course Ernesto is in love with Norina. Don Pasquale's proposed means of disinheriting his nephew is, despite his advancing years and lifelong bachelorhood, for himself to marry and to raise a family. Hereabouts modern producers and translators are often unable to resist inserting a classic (i.e. well-worn) joke. I have in recent years seen two English language productions in which an exchange along the following lines has been inserted. Don Pasquale seeks the medical advice of Dr Malatesta because, not unreasonably, he fears that at his age his generative powers could be diminished. Dr Malatesta reassures him on this matter as follows:

Don Pasquale: Do you think that at my age I shall be able to beget children, doctor?
Dr Malatesta: All will be well if you take viagra.
Don Pasquale: Viagra? Will I be able to get it over the counter?
Dr Malatesta: Ah! You will probably need two viagra for that.

There are of course those who hold that the old jokes are the best.

However, Dr Malatesta is behaving unprofessionally. He is secretly in league with Ernesto and is defrauding his wealthy patient. The doctor claims to have found just the bride for Don Pasquale, a quiet and pretty young girl called 'Sofronia' at present living in a convent. In fact the 'pure maiden Sofronia' is none other than Norina in disguise.

Once the sham wedding ceremony has taken place, and Don Pasquale is supposedly married, the character of Sofronia changes from that of a demure innocent into a profligate spendthrift and raging termagant who does not hesitate, if she feels like it, to attack Don Pasquale physically. By the time Don Pasquale has had a lute smashed over his head, he pleads for the doctor somehow to get him out of the mess.

In the end, of course, matters are put to rights. The marriage is revealed as bogus; Don Pasquale, relieved at being free, gives his blessing to the union of Ernesto with Norina; and the opera closes with Norina delivering to the audience the moral of the tale: 'A man who marries when he is old is weak in the head and asking for trouble'. Medically of course there is a different, but very important message, unstated in the opera. A doctor's first duty should be to his patient. Someone behaving as Dr Malatesta does here is asking for trouble of a different sort with the General Medical Council.

A MEDICINAL CHEMIST

JANÁČEK: THE MAKROPULOS CASE 1926

Operatic doctors are, as we have seen, often, although fortunately not uniformly, undistinguished. The doctor to be considered here, a medicinal chemist, is very different. He would, had he lived in the appropriate era, almost certainly have been awarded the Nobel Prize for medicine. The opera is *The Makropulos Case*, composed by Janáček to his own libretto after the play by Karel Čapek. The doctor does not appear on stage, although he is much talked of, and his medical achievements govern the whole affair.

The action is set in Prague in 1922. The central character, Emilia Marty, soprano, is a famous opera singer, and is now 337 years old. Her father was Hieronymus Makropulos, physician to the Holy Roman Emperor Rudolf II. The Emperor had asked Dr Makropulos to find a means of enabling him to live forever. Nowadays persons with such ambitions would probably be directed to a cardiovascular epidemiologist, who would advise the consumption of substantial amounts of fresh fruit and vegetables, restricted intake of salt and alcohol, and the avoidance of cigarette smoking. Whatever benefits might accrue from such a regime, there would certainly be conveyed to the recipient at least the impression of longevity, albeit perhaps tedious.

Dr Makropulos was however more forthright, and he developed a chemical compound which was to be administered for this purpose. However, the Emperor Rudolf insisted that the doctor first try out the drug on his own daughter, Elina. Elina fell sick, and her father was imprisoned as a charlatan. But Elina unexpectedly recovered and she then escaped with the formula.

Elina subsequently trained as a singer, and with centuries to perfect her technique has now in 1922 become one of the greatest operatic sopranos of all time. Moving from country to country to avoid suspicion, she has undergone frequent changes of name, though always retaining the initials E.M. (Interestingly, and perhaps surprisingly, I can find no evidence that the distinguished real-life soprano Eva Marton has ever sung this role.)

As the opera begins Elina Makropulos, alias Emilia Marty, senses she is ageing, and she urgently requires a further dose of the elixir. She has therefore returned

The Makropulos Case: The ageing Emilia Marty (Catherine Wilson) with the tenor Albert Gregor (Mark Hamilton). Albert Gregor is the descendant of an illegitimate child she bore in the 19th century when calling herself Elian MacGregor. Scottish Opera, 1981. Photo: Eric Thorburn.

to Prague to recover the formula, which is inscribed on a document known by her to be in the house of one Baron Prus, a baritone. Yet although the document is found, she then decides that she has had enough. She wishes now to live no longer, and she donates the formula to Kristina, a young aspiring soprano. However, Kristina does not want to emulate Elina's longevity, and she destroys the document. Elina dies. Dr Hieronymus Makropulos never was awarded the Nobel Prize he so richly deserved.

23

A CANINE GENERAL PRACTITIONER

ANNE DUDLEY: THE DOCTOR'S TALE 2011

Anne Dudley's opera *The Doctor's Tale*, to a libretto by Terry Jones, tells of a therapeutically successful general practitioner (tenor), beloved by his patients, who falls foul of the General Medical Council because he is a dog. The General Medical Council seeks to have him erased from the medical register; preferably indeed put down, despite his unquestioned professional competence.

The Councillors, in their grey suits, make for ready operatic villains, as does the canine doctor for hero. Nevertheless, some sympathy should be afforded to the General Medical Council in this instance. It would not do for animal pets, however domesticated, to take over the running of even a part of the National Health Service.

The Doctor's Tale: The canine general practitioner (Darren Abrahams) with his receptionist. Royal Opera House, 2011. Photo: © Catherine Ashmore.

24

A PRIVATE PHYSICIAN

VERDI: LA TRAVIATA 1853

A physician in private practice might be expected to command some deference, both from patients and from the public. We encounter a person who initially appears to be just such a doctor in Verdi's *La traviata* of 1853, composed to a libretto by Piave after both a novel and a play by Alexandre Dumas fils, *La dame aux camélias* (sic: Dumas insisted on spelling the name of those flowers in that idiosyncratic fashion).

One of the most prevalent diseases of the 19th century for which then there was no cure was consumption – pulmonary tuberculosis. Many a Victorian literary, dramatic, and operatic heroine died from that affliction. Violetta, the soprano courtesan of the Parisian demi-monde in *La traviata*, is a typical sufferer. In the opera she is under the care of Dr Grenvil (bass).

By the time of the last act, Violetta is dying of consumption. She has lost her good looks and most of her fortune, and she is lying in her bed in a shabby apartment, attended only by her faithful maid. It is early morning. Dr Grenvil arrives to examine his patient. Dr Grenvil comforts Violetta, although he observes, and warns the maid, that she is deteriorating rapidly. He says he will return later in the day. Dr Grenvil does indeed return later, but despite his ministrations, Violetta dies.

It is possible at this point to pursue a little medical research. As was recounted in Chapter 13, another 19th-century Parisian operatic heroine, Mimì, dies from pulmonary tuberculosis, but in the absence of a doctor. In Puccini's *La bohème* the time taken for Mimì to die in the last act, in a recording conducted by Thomas Beecham wherein Mimì is sung by Victoria de los Angeles, is 19 minutes. In Leoncavallo's version of *La bohème*, as conducted by Heinz Wallberg and with Mimì sung by Lucia Popp, the heroine lasts a mere 14 minutes. By contrast, in *La traviata*, where a doctor is in attendance, the patient, Violetta, as sung for example by Ileana Cotrubas in a performance conducted by Carlos Kleiber, takes 25 minutes to die. So is demonstrated the beneficial therapeutic value of a doctor, even for a disease which was then devoid of effective drug treatment. This analytical approach is nowadays termed 'evidence-based medicine', a method with some fervent advocates. Hence Dr Grenvil can perhaps lay claim to a measure, albeit modest, of therapeutic effectiveness.

It remains necessary to explain the rather odd life that Dr Grenvil leads in the

La traviata: Dr Grenvil (Alan Fairs) treats the dying Violetta (Carmen Giannattasio). Scottish Opera, 2008. Photo: Drew Farrell.

opera *La traviata.* In Acts I and II Dr Grenvil appears to be a physician in very lucrative private practice, since he seems able to afford to attend the expensive parties at which the courtesans entertain their aristocratic clients, or 'protectors', as those wealthy patrons were usually termed. Even so, in those first two acts Dr Grenvil's actions are by no means professional, and include gambling and heavy drinking. And then, in Act III, we find this same Dr Grenvil plodding around the streets of Paris at seven o'clock in the morning doing his house calls, a circumstance seemingly at odds with what had earlier appeared as a highly remunerative private practice. The distinguished musicologist and critic Ernest Newman's view of the matter was that Verdi had been obliged to engage the services of a bass singer to perform the role of Dr Grenvil in Act III.[1] Thus saddled with that singer, Verdi thought that he might as well provide employment for him also in Acts I and II, and so in those first two acts Dr Grenvil is invited to various lavish, if louche, parties.

Newman's explanation seems, however, to be wrong. In 2008, Scottish Opera staged a new production of *La traviata,* directed by David McVicar, and the matter was gone into more carefully. In 2003, David McVicar had directed a play, *Camille,* by Neil Bartlett, concerning the same tale. The character Dr Grenvil is seemingly based on the activities of a real person, Dr Koreff, who is depicted in that play. Dr Koreff apparently did once obtain a genuine medical qualification. He practised homeopathy and mesmerism (mesmerism is discussed in Chapter 29) and attached himself to the Parisian demi-monde. According to one account (there are many inconsistencies), Dr Koreff was officially disbarred from medical practice for performing an illegal abortion, although he continued as a quack, and treated venereal disease in both the courtesans and their clients.

Despite the numerous uncertainties, this information concerning Dr Koreff does seem to provide a more likely explanation for the way Dr Grenvil is presented in Verdi's opera.

1.   Newman. See Preface note 13, p. 584.

25

THE MYSTERIOUS DEATH OF A WRITER

DOMINICK ARGENTO: THE VOYAGE OF EDGAR ALLAN POE 1976
The American writer Edgar Allan Poe was born probably, but not certainly, in Boston, Massachusetts in January 1809. On one occasion he himself claimed to have been born in 1813, but that seems unlikely, as it would have been two years after the death of his mother. His eventful, but frequently disreputable, career included heavy gambling, dishonourable discharge from West Point, and alcoholism. He married his thirteen-year-old cousin, Virginia, in 1836; she died in 1847. Poe seems to have been musically knowledgeable, and musicians unquestionably responded to his literary work. There are known to be over 250 musical compositions based on his writings; at least 80 per cent of his poems have been set to music. Chapter 26 considers three operatic versions of his story *The Fall of the House of Usher*. Poe died in mysterious circumstances. He reportedly left Richmond, Virginia, early on 27 September 1849 by ship for the one-day voyage to Baltimore. He was found on 3 October, semiconscious in a Baltimore street, seemingly drunk. He was admitted violently delirious to hospital, where he died on 7 October. Dominick Argento's two-act opera, to a libretto by Charles Nolte, deals with the supposed events leading up to Poe's death.

The action takes place on the dockside at Richmond and aboard a vessel apparently sailing from there. The opera opens with the Doctor (tenor) recalling his last encounter with Poe (also tenor) at the quay. Poe, ill and feverish, plans to sail to Baltimore that night, despite the Doctor's belief that no ship is scheduled to depart. Poe insists that his literary executor Griswold (baritone) had told him of one. The Doctor warns him against Griswold; he cautions him also to desist from alcohol.

Alone on the quayside, Poe awaits the ship. A ghostly vessel appears. Strange phantoms drift across its decks and beckon Poe aboard. He embarks, and the ship disappears into the mist.

In the ship's lounge, a small troupe of actors is presenting a melodrama. Poe realises that it is a re-enactment of his own mother's death when he was a child. The scene takes on a reality into which he is drawn.

Amid further fantasies, Griswold appears. Poe is accused of engineering his own wife's death so as to inspire his literary creativity. He is tried, with Griswold as judge. Enraged, Poe attempts to stab Griswold, who turns out to be simply an image in a mirror. The reflection changes to that of Poe himself, which extends a seemingly welcoming arm to receive his blows.

The following dawn finds Poe once more alone on the quayside. Unseen by Poe, Griswold emerges from the shadows and watches. Poe hears the voice of his dead wife Virginia (soprano) singing to him. Virginia's voice dies away and Poe sinks lifeless. The Doctor explains that Poe had wished to embark on the previous evening, but Griswold affirms that no ship departed. Griswold disappears into the dark, leaving the Doctor kneeling by the body of Poe.

The nightmarish events are presented via a score based on a free application of dodecaphonic music. The plot has been criticised as being confused, although given the subject matter that could be a harsh judgement. Poe's actual life was hardly a model of rectitude to be portrayed with narrative clarity. Poe experiencing a nightmare would surely involve some obscurities. More favourably, this work has been regarded as one of the most musico-dramatically successful operas composed in the twelve-note idiom.

A RESIDENT FAMILY DOCTOR AND A MISTAKEN DIAGNOSIS

DEBUSSY 1918, SITSKY 1965, GLASS 1988: THE FALL OF THE HOUSE OF USHER

The American writer Edgar Allan Poe and Argento's opera dealing with his death were discussed in the previous chapter. One of the best-known of Poe's tales of grotesque sinister horror is *The Fall of the House of Usher*, which appeared in *Burton's Gentleman's Magazine* in 1839.

The story has been set as an opera on at least three occasions. Claude Debussy prepared from the tale his own libretto, in French, and worked on the music from 1909 until his death in 1918. This opera remains incomplete. Some sections of the libretto have no music; in other places there are alternative textual and musical versions, with little or no indication of Debussy's preference. For those reasons, attempts to prepare a posthumous performing version have encountered serious problems. However, Debussy's opera was staged at New Haven, Connecticut, in 1977, in a reconstruction by Carolyn Abbate. In 2006, Robert Orledge put together another version which was given in a highly praised production by Phyllida Lloyd at the Bregenz Festival. Debussy's four characters are the Narrator, Roderick and the Doctor (all baritones) and Madeline (soprano).

Larry Sitsky's one-act opera of the same title, to an English text by Gwen Harwood, dates from 1965. Sitsky cast the Narrator as tenor, Roderick as baritone, and Madeline as soprano; he excluded the Doctor.

Philip Glass composed his chamber opera of 1988 to an English libretto by Arthur Yorinks. Glass cast the Narrator (whom he called William) as tenor, Roderick as baritone, Madeline as soprano, and the Doctor as tenor.

Poe's story, and hence the derived operas, are remarkable for the numerous and wide range of medical conditions and diagnoses they contain. To these must be added one spectacular misdiagnosis, which, as shall be seen, was to have catastrophic consequences. Roderick Usher and his twin sister Madeline are both of them unmarried and childless; they are the last of their genealogical line, the House of Usher. The pair of them live in their gloomy crumbling castle. The term 'House of Usher' is thus applied both to that castle and to the family lineage, each soon to become extinct. The Narrator in the story, an old school friend of Roderick Usher, is summoned by Roderick to the castle. Roderick Usher has sensed an impending disaster which in some vague way he hopes that his visiting friend can help to avert.

A famous picture by Arthur Rackham shows the Narrator arriving on horseback at the castle. He observes as he approaches that neither the building nor the grounds have been well maintained. There are numerous dead trees which should have been felled but have not. The moat is stagnant. The castle walls are heavily infested with fungus; clearly there is urgent need of the attentions of a company such as Rentokil. Prominently shown in Rackham's painting is an irregular crack in one of the castle walls. This defect in the fabric will later assume considerable importance.

Roderick Usher is found by his friend to be suffering from numerous medical disabilities. He has severe mental depression. He has a morbid hyperacuity of all five senses: he can bear hardly anything to touch his skin; he shuns the light; he can tolerate the sounds only of some soft-stringed instruments such as the guitar (he remains very fond nevertheless of a tune by Weber); the scents of flowers are unbearable to him; he can endure only the most insipid food. In addition to all these problems he has for several years been afflicted with agoraphobia – that is, a psychological dread of leaving his dwelling. It is about this point that the Narrator, who seems to be rather a perceptive fellow, begins to suspect that his stay at the House of Usher is unlikely to be especially convivial.

That is even before he meets Roderick Usher's sister Madeline. Madeline is wasting away with what would nowadays be called anorexia nervosa, a condition wherein the patient refuses to eat. Madeline also suffers from attacks of catalepsy, a disease marked by the sudden arrest of all movements and the prolonged maintenance of distorted physical postures. From time to time, and simultaneous with her episodes of catalepsy, Madeline enters a trance-like mental state. Apparently there had once existed an incestuous relationship between Roderick and his sister, although their present torpor seemingly now precludes sexual activity.

In Poe's tale the strange household includes also a resident family physician. This doctor is described by Poe as evincing a mixture of medical perplexity and low cunning. Poe's phraseology suggests that he regards this conjunction as quite extraordinary, although in my experience the combination of perplexity and low cunning is by no means unusual in the medical world. Moreover, I can readily accept that many physicians would be perplexed if faced with the range of therapeutic problems that this particular family doctor is required to confront. At one time, it transpires, Madeline had shared her sexual favours also with the doctor. This relationship, like that involving her brother, has now also lapsed with the general inertia.

The Narrator, with notable fortitude, endures the macabre ambience of the House of Usher for what appear to be several weeks. Then one evening he is abruptly informed by Roderick that Madeline is no more. We are to understand that she had been found unrousable and was duly pronounced dead by the Doctor.

Roderick then proposes a bizarre procedure. He will keep Madeline's corpse, in its coffin, in the house for two weeks before the final interment. The Narrator uneasily accedes to this extraordinary suggestion. He and Roderick bear the body in its coffin to a remote windowless room lined with copper, set the coffin on trestles, close the coffin lid on Madeline's wan face, screw down the lid, and then depart, closing the massive door of the vault behind them.

Over the next week Roderick Usher becomes more and more distracted. Then a wild storm arises one night. The sleepless Narrator rises fitfully from his bed and encounters the now quite deranged Roderick. He feels compelled to read to his host an old grisly narrative, *The Mad Trist*, of Sir Launcelot Canning. Roderick could of course perfectly well, if he wished, and despite his disabilities, have read the story for himself, but presumably for dramatic reasons it is necessary for it to be read to him. At the climax of the reading a distant, but increasingly loud, knocking sound obtrudes. Roderick announces that he has heard this frightening noise several times in recent nights, and he fears that it may come from the coffin of his sister, who he now dreads has in error been entombed while still alive.

There is an abrupt rasping crash as of the rending of the wooden lid of the coffin; there can be heard the grating of the hinges of the door of her prison; and then suddenly, at the threshold, there stands the enshrouded figure of Madeline in blood-stained white robes. She reels for a moment, then with a horrible moan, falls upon her brother, and, in her final death throes, carries him, now also a corpse, to the floor.

The Narrator flees in terror out into the storm. There is (of course) a blood-red moon disclosed intermittently amid the racing clouds. And then the great fissure in the castle wall, to which I drew attention earlier, splits asunder, and the building collapses into the moat. The House of Usher, the castle and the genealogical line, both have fallen, for ever.

I have described in Chapter 13 Puccini's opera *Gianni Schicchi*. There the doctor, one Spinelloccio, makes the converse mistake, supposing old Buoso Donati still to be alive when he is in fact dead, and so enabling Gianni Schicchi and Buoso's relatives to prepare a fraudulent will. The very opposite medical error in *The Fall of the House of Usher* is more horrible and more catastrophic in its consequences. One of Madeline's cataleptic trances has been mistaken for her death, and she has hence been consigned, still alive, to her coffin.

Poe's tale did of course provide a most apt vehicle for the three very different, yet each in their contrasted fashions, appropriate, musical approaches of Larry Sitsky, Philip Glass, and Claude Debussy. Sitsky's opera has been described as powerfully dramatic in its instrumental writing, which is based on ten twelve-note rows, albeit the libretto 'is vocally stilted'. Glass's chamber orchestration of a chromatic score tellingly evokes the eerie, doom-laden drama. I think it is especially regrettable that Debussy never provided a definitive version. *The Fall of the House of Usher* (*La chute de la Maison Usher* as he called it) would have made an interesting complement to his sole completed opera, *Pelléas et Mélisande*.

27

A DOCTOR ASSAULTED

PROKOFIEV: WAR AND PEACE 1944/1959/2010

I shall turn now to what may, no doubt rather perversely, be considered an entertaining prospect; a doctor assaulted by his patient. An interesting, if perhaps disturbing, feature of medicine as practised today is an increasing tendency for patients to attack physically both doctors and nurses. This seems, not surprisingly, to be most prevalent in the accident and emergency departments of hospitals late at night, but has also happened from time to time even in general practitioners' surgeries. This disconcerting development is reflected in the prominent notices now displayed in hospitals and clinics, warning patients not to abuse doctors or nurses either verbally or physically. Such exhortations are, in my opinion, more likely to foment rather than discourage those attacks, being akin to the apocryphal signboards of my childhood: 'It is forbidden to throw stones at this notice'. I did at any rate suppose them to be apocryphal until I came across a photograph taken at the Norfolk Broads in the summer of 2009 asking: 'Please do not throw stones at this sign. Thank you'. Evidently the inhabitants of Norfolk are more urbane than those further north.

Assaults on the doctor by a patient were unknown in my day, even in rough parts of cities; I neither experienced nor heard of an instance. Doctors were, understandably, sometimes tempted to attack patients, but that was, however justifiable, absolutely forbidden (but see Chapter 11). I was therefore surprised to find that an attack on a doctor had been presented on the operatic stage, with the supposed incident dating from the early years of the 19th century.

The opera is Prokofiev's *War and Peace*, of which a portion was played in 1944; the first really complete performance was not until 1959.[1] The libretto of the opera was written by Prokofiev himself in collaboration with Mira Mendelson after Tolstoy's monumental novel of 1869.

Tolstoy's novel *War and Peace* deals with events and personalities in Russia before, during, and after the time of Napoleon's invasion, that is, from 1805 through to 1820. Prokofiev's derived opera has distinct similarities to those of his predecessors as composers who also dealt with aspects of Russian history. Glinka's *A Life for the Tsar* and Moussorgsky's *Khovanshchina* would be good examples as forerunners. The opera *War and Peace* comprises thirteen scenes and an epigraph. The assault on the doctor is described in Part I Scene 7.[2] In the opera the incident is presented as a reminiscence by the victim, Dr Métivier, a baritone, whose assailant was the old Prince Nikolai Bolkonsky, a bass. A fuller and rather clearer account is given in the original novel.

Dr Métivier was a French doctor living in Moscow in 1811; he was tall, handsome, courteous, and oozing charm. In short, he was a smoothie. Largely because of those qualities he was widely considered to be an extraordinarily clever doctor. In fact, none of the attributes denotes professional skill, although patients frequently make that erroneous assumption, as is attested by the considerable fortunes often acquired by doctors of distinctly modest accomplishments, for example in Harley Street private practice.

Old Prince Bolkonsky had for many years ridiculed medicine, a very sensible perception especially in Moscow at that time. But then he had been persuaded to permit Dr Métivier to visit him; he slowly grew accustomed to and less suspicious of Dr Métivier, and the doctor started to attend on the old Prince twice a week. Nominally then, Prince Bolkonsky had become Dr Métivier's patient, despite there being no ailment and no therapy.

What Dr Métivier should have recognised, but did not, was that the old Prince was unpredictably disposed to ill-temper. And Prince Bolkonsky was in just such a foul mood on St Nikolai's Day 1811, his name-day. On that day all Moscow drove up to the Prince's front door, but he had given strict orders that no one whose name was absent from a very select list he had prepared was to be admitted. Dr Métivier's name was not on that list.

Dr Métivier nevertheless arrived in the morning with his felicitations, and he considered himself to be entitled, as the Prince's doctor, to be allowed in. This was not a prudent assumption. Despite warnings from the Prince's daughter, Princess Maria (mezzo-soprano), the Doctor insisted, and went in to see the old man in his study. The Princess remained anxiously outside. At first the only sound she heard was that of Dr Métivier's voice, then her father's, then both voices simultaneously, then her father shouting. Suddenly the door flew open, and on the threshold appeared the handsome figure of the now terrified Dr Métivier, his cravat torn aside and his collar awry, followed by the Prince in his skull-cap and dressing-gown, his face distorted with rage and the pupils of his eyes dilated. 'You don't see it?' yelled the Prince. 'Well I do! French spy, slave of Bonaparte, spy, spy! Get out of my house – get out, I tell you!'[3] And he slammed the door on the ashen-faced, panic-stricken physician. Dr Métivier could sometimes be quite quick on the uptake. He concluded from these pleasantries that Prince Bolkonsky was no longer a patient on his list. And there, however improbably, was a 21st-century medico-social problem foreseen within the Russian aristocracy some 200 years earlier.

---

1. On 22 January 2010, at the Theatre Royal Glasgow, the world premiere of the original version, shorn of its Stalinist accretions, in an edition by Rita McAllister, was given in a joint production between Scottish Opera, the Royal Scottish Academy of Music and Drama, and the Rostov State Conservatoire.
2. In the 2010 Rita McAllister edition, the assault is in Part I Scene 6.
3. The translation here is by Rosemary Edmonds.

28

A DOCTOR MURDERED

HARRISON BIRTWISTLE: PUNCH AND JUDY 1968

The murder of a doctor occurs in Birtwistle's opera *Punch and Judy* of 1968, composed to a libretto by Stephen Pruslin. I can confidently assert that this opera, *Punch and Judy,* is not to everyone's taste. At the premiere at the Aldeburgh Festival, Benjamin Britten and Peter Pears ostentatiously left their seats in mid-performance.[1] Yet there are others, for instance the critic Andrew Porter, who consider it to be a splendid piece.[2]

Punch and Judy broke away decisively from the traditional narrative form so typical of 19th- and early 20th-century opera. I have been able to find no evidence that Pierre Boulez was at first aware of this venture by Birtwistle and Pruslin, although they would almost certainly have known and understood the views of Boulez concerning contemporaneous operatic composition and performance. It was the impact of hearing scores by Boulez in 1957 that encouraged Birtwistle to turn from clarinet playing to composition, and Birtwistle went on to attend the Darmstadt summer courses where Boulez was a prominent teacher.

Boulez set out three precepts essential for the achievement of what, in his view, would be a truly modern opera.[3] First, the libretto must be conceived directly for the musical theatre, and not be an adaptation of pre-existent literary material; with every word and note the music should be integral with the text. Second, the director must be uninhibitedly innovative. Third, the performance should be on a small stage where 'one could risk all kind of things'.

In *Punch and Judy* Birtwistle and Pruslin accorded closely with those notions of Boulez. The libretto was intricately original, saturated with alliterations and puns; by no means a simple account of the traditional children's Punch and Judy puppet play. The director Anthony Besch and the designer Peter Rice were certainly distinctively innovative. The Aldeburgh Jubilee Hall theatre and stage were undoubtedly small.

Punch and Judy was then a highly original opera. It has just one act, and a fifteen-piece orchestra. In the course of the work Punch commits a whole series of murders: of his and Judy's baby; of Judy herself; of the Lawyer; of the Doctor; of the Choregos or Chorus; and finally, by way of a cunning stratagem, of the hangman Jack Ketch. Throughout Punch makes repeated amorous advances towards Pretty Polly, and eventually is at the end successful and gains Pretty Polly's hand. The opera thus shows Punch as capable variously of viciousness or tenderness. The work can be, and has been, seen as an amoral fable, depicting the ultimate triumph of evil.

The libretto, verbally complex, is dramatically symmetrical, with rigorous classical proportions. It is in the course of what is termed Melodrama II that the Doctor is murdered. Punch (high baritone) is confronted by the Lawyer (high tenor) and the Doctor (deep bass). These two professional men emphasise to Punch:

> The law of the land is the medicine of mankind ...
> The medicine of the land is the law of mankind ... etc., etc.

It will be evident here that the librettist Pruslin, whatever his literary virtuosity, falls rather short of the evocative poetic elegance of Shakespeare.

Punch is having none of such pontificating by the Lawyer and the Doctor, and he murders them both, using as his weapons a quill pen for the Lawyer and a hypodermic syringe for the Doctor. These homicidal actions by Punch can resonate strongly with audiences. That these two pompous fellows meet their ends through the agency of their own professional equipment is considered to be most apposite. Some have expressed regret that such an outcome is not more frequent. Of course, in 1968, when this opera was first performed, physical assaults on doctors were much less prevalent than they are today.

1. Carpenter, H., *Benjamin Britten*, Scribners, New York, 1992, p. 480.
2. Porter, A., *Opera* 2008: 59: 702.
3. Boulez, P. Interview for *Der Spiegel*, 25 September 1967.

29

SOME MORE MEDICAL IMPOSTORS

A diagnostically and therapeutically very successful medical impostor was described in Chapter 6. The impostors in the three operas here display variable expertise.

MOZART: COSÌ FAN TUTTE 1790

In opera can be encountered medical impostors treating real patients, as well as the converse, genuine doctors dealing with outright malingerers. In Mozart's *Così fan tutte* those two fraudulent circumstances are combined, with a supposed doctor, who is in reality an unqualified pretender, treating two patients who are deliberately feigning illness. Moreover, that amalgamation of medical malfeasance is compounded by the form of therapy administered, which is the now thoroughly discredited mesmerism.

Franz Anton Mesmer was born at Rudolfzell by Lake Constance in 1734. In his early years Mesmer had been much influenced by a Jesuit priest called Father Maximilian Hell. Father Hell's name could, one might suppose, have warned Mesmer, although it is in fact innocuous in German, in which language 'hell' simply means 'clear' or 'bright'. Father Hell had, with some apparent success, used magnets for treating the sick. Thus encouraged, Mesmer submitted, for his medical graduation at Vienna in 1765, a dissertation concerning the influence of the planets on the human body, in which he proposed that a magnetic fluid pervaded the universe, and affected particularly the nervous system of man and animals.

Dr Mesmer then proceeded in Vienna to build up a lucrative medical practice involving magnetism which, he claimed, might purposefully divert the course of the supposed magnetic fluid, and, if correctly applied, benefit the patient. Dr Mesmer's therapeutic use of magnets was not, however, approved of by the Viennese medical establishment, and in 1778 he was obliged to move to Paris.[1]

In Paris he conducted treatment sessions open to the public, at which his patients sat round a special tub or baquet. A contemporary illustration shows one of these therapeutic events in progress, with the patients clutching iron rods

Cosi fan tutte: Despina (Elizabeth Gale) as a counterfeit doctor employs mesmerism to treat the malingering Ferrando (Maldwyn Davies) and Guglielmo (Stephen Page). Fiordiligi (Marie Slorach) and Dorabella (Clare Shearer) worry. Don Alfonso (Andrew Shore) is overcome by mirth. Scottish Opera, 1988. Photo: Eric Thorburn.

through which the magnetic fluid was alleged to travel. Mesmer approached his patients strangely clad in lilac-coloured silk and carrying an iron wand or magnet which he waved over them so as to encourage the magnetic fluid to flow in the right direction. Quite often at these sessions patients entered a trance or suffered convulsions. Nevertheless, Dr Mesmer also achieved several apparent cures.

Not surprisingly, all of this excited great public interest as well as a good deal of professional medical jealousy. Consequently, King Louis XVI ordered the French Académie des Sciences to set up a Commission to look into the whole affair. The Commission contained some famous and distinguished persons. Included was the physicist and polymath Benjamin Franklin, who was at that time American Ambassador in Paris. Franklin had, among numerous interests, studied electrical phenomena, especially those of thunderstorms. Present also was the prominent chemist Lavoisier, the discoverer of oxygen. Another commissioner was a physician, Dr Joseph Guillotin, he who promulgated the penal use of the guillotine. Interestingly, although it is often put about that Dr Guillotin did himself die at the guillotine, that is not correct; he passed away peacefully in his bed. Lavoisier was, however, later guillotined, although for reasons unconnected with the enquiry into the activities of Dr Mesmer. Also subsequently guillotined was King Louis XVI.

The Report of the Commission in 1784 rejected Mesmer's magnetic theories, attributing the convulsions and cures that his treatment evoked to the effect of imagination. That was I think a sound judgement for its date. There is no way that the members of the Commission could have predicted the discovery of nuclear magnetic resonance in 1946, or that magnetic resonance imaging would come to be widely employed as an investigative method in clinical medicine. Most pertinently to the opera considered here, that 1784 Parisian Commission pointed out the danger of sexual exploitation of susceptible subjects by mesmerism because of the close rapport often established between the doctor and the patient in the course of mesmeric treatment.

It will therefore be evident that mesmerism was a very topical issue at the time when Da Ponte was writing the libretto of *Così fan tutte* for Mozart. That opera had its first performance in Vienna in January 1790, a particularly appropriate locale given that mesmerism had originated in that city.

The story of the opera involves two sisters, Fiordiligi (soprano) and Dorabella (mezzo-soprano). They swear undying love to their respective fiancés, Guglielmo (baritone) and Ferrando (tenor). However, the sceptical older bachelor Don Alfonso (bass) wagers that the affirmed fidelity of the girls is fragile. The bet takes the form of the two young men ostensibly leaving for the army, then returning in disguise, with each proceeding to woo the other's girl.

The early resistance of the two ladies is softened by Guglielmo and Ferrando pretending to poison themselves with arsenic in grief because of their initially unrequited love. In great alarm the girls dispatch their maid Despina to fetch a doctor. Despina herself returns disguised as a doctor, and she proceeds to revive the two fake suicides by way of mesmerism. Da Ponte's libretto is very clear at this point concerning Mesmer, his magnet, and his exploits in Vienna and Paris. Perhaps not surprisingly, but disappointingly, present-day producers often deviate from Da Ponte's stage directions.

The sexual susceptibilities predicted by the 1784 Commission are realised in the opera. The fidelity of the two girls weakens from there on, and each falls in love with the other's fiancé. There follows a mock wedding ceremony with the original pairs crossed over, whereupon the two men unmask, to the great embarrassment and consternation of their supposed wives. Thus Don Alfonso wins his bet; all four lovers are wiser and sadder; and we in the audience are left at the end unsure of the definitive pairings.

Mesmerism as such is no longer in vogue as a form of medical treatment, although some cynical doctors allege that the essential features persist, albeit with different terminology, in the present-day psychotherapeutic repertoire. Nuclear magnetic resonance and magnetic resonance imaging are, as they say, part of another story.

BIZET: LE DOCTEUR MIRACLE 1857

In this opera, as in the real world of medicine and medical politics (if the latter can be described as being part of the real world), is to be seen that a very substantial therapeutic reputation can be achieved by first promulgating fearfulness of, and then apparently curing, an entirely bogus, so-called deadly, disease.

In the opera Silvio (tenor), a simple soldier, is in love with Laurette (soprano), the daughter of a wealthy magistrate (baritone), who of course wishes Laurette to have nothing to do with Silvio. Silvio thus disguises himself, is engaged by the family as a cook, and prepares for them an omelette. The operatic centrepiece is the 'omelette quartet', a solemn mock-heroic invocation to the dish, much in the manner of Robert Burns and the haggis. The omelette is eaten. But then, Silvio's true identity is discovered, he is dismissed, and, perhaps not surprisingly, the gastronomic quality of the omelette is questioned. The diners now find that the omelette did not taste so well as they had at first thought.

The banished Silvio has, however, a further ploy. He sends a message (in modern productions by mobile telephone) informing the family that the omelette was seriously poisoned and that only the famous Dr Miracle can help. Dr Miracle is of course summoned, and thus Silvio returns, disguised this time as the fake Dr Miracle. At this point nearly all productions emphasise the power of suggestion. Most of the family are by now rolling about in supposed agony, despite the omelette not, in reality, being poisoned.

Silvio, alias Dr Miracle, extracts a promise of the hand of Laurette in exchange for the cure. Laurette, who has by now rumbled the true identity of Dr Miracle, eagerly agrees. A counterfeit medicine is administered and all are restored to health, which of course they had never lost in the first place. So the tenor, Silvio, gets his girl. And subsequently, as in the real world, Dr Miracle, although entirely bogus, is in great professional demand.

GOUNOD: LE MÉDECIN MALGRÉ LUI 1858

In this work is to be met the first and, so far as I am aware, the only operatic character to have had both the title and the duties of a doctor thrust unwillingly upon him. The opera is *Le médecin malgré lui* (*The Doctor in Spite of Himself*), composed by Gounod in 1858 to a libretto by Barbier and Carré after the 1666 play of that name by Molière. Molière, otherwise known by his real name Jean-Baptiste Poquelin, was, as discussed in Chapter 6, particularly severe on the medical profession. His view of the pompous futility of doctors was not a flattering one. Gounod's opera, derived very closely from Molière's play, displays Molière's dramatic talents to superb effect. Remarkably, the Parisian Comédie-Française initially tried to block performances of Gounod's opera, because the librettists used Molière's text almost verbatim for long stretches of the spoken dialogue, and had also based the sung lyrics closely on the original play. This was felt by some malcontents to be disrespectful to Molière. The notion of regarding the memory and reputation of Molière of all people with polite diplomatic reverence seems to me to involve a particularly obtuse, indeed convoluted, line of reasoning. Not surprisingly, certainly gratifyingly, the attempted embargo failed.

In the various quotations I shall give here from Gounod's opera, I have taken the English translation of the libretto prepared by two Americans, Mark Herman and Ronnie Apter in 1979 for a production in New York. The approach by

Herman and Apter is declared by them in the preface to that translation, in which they affected an antique style of English: 'Matter and Manner were so closely Subjoyned, that by taking any Course other than that of translating in the style of the Time, they wou'd wrong M. Molière, to avoid which they Resolved to Use the language of his Age'. And this they did.

The central figure in the opera is Sganarelle, a baritone, who is a cutter, gatherer, and binder of firewood. Sganarelle has a high opinion of himself: 'You will never find a gatherer of wood with my choice turn of mind, Who had served for years a notable physician, And can dispute a subtle point with a scholarly art, And who has learned a chapter of his Latin book by heart'.

Sganarelle is also given to drunkenness and to beating his wife, the soprano Martine. Those latter misdeeds are, however, seen by Martine herself as a private domestic matter. When a neighbour, M. Robert, attempts to intervene in one such assault he is sent packing by Martine: 'Well Sir, and I have a mind to be beat, what then? What is it to you?' Even so, Martine does resent her husband's abusive behaviour: 'Battered women, thrashed by their husbands, have means to come by their revenge!' And Martine is soon duly presented with just such an opportunity.

Lucinde is the daughter of Géronte, bass, a rich landowner. Lucinde is a soprano, although this is not immediately evident to the audience, because Lucinde has been struck dumb. Her disability is, however, feigned. The father Geronte has forbidden her to marry, indeed even to meet, her lover Léandre, a tenor, because Léandre is poor and has uncertain prospects (this is therefore a stock operatic situation). Hence Lucinde sulkily pretends that she has lost the power of speech.

Géronte fails to recognise what is going on, that his daughter's loss of voice is simulated, and is a consequence of his own strict disciplinary actions, and he sends two of his servants, Valère, a baritone, and Lucas, a tenor, to seek out a doctor who can cure Lucinde's apparent speech disorder. Hereabouts Molière stoops to what was, especially for him, a rather clumsy dramatic device; evidently he could not find a more plausible way of carrying the story forward. It must of course be conceded that this was long before the introduction of NHS 24, or of similar organisations in France; of *Yellow Pages*; or of the World Wide Web. Hence Molière has Géronte dispatch Valère and Lucas to scour the countryside for a doctor.

Martine encounters the pair, and seizes her chance. She tells Valère and Lucas that her husband Sganarelle, although he pretends to ignorance, and spends his time cutting wood, is in reality a learned and distinguished physician, who has in the past achieved some near miraculous cures. However, he can be induced to practice his medical art only if he is beaten. Hence Valère and Lucas duly beat up Sganarelle. Sganarelle sensibly gives way: 'I shall take, to appease you, my degree by decree, and for you be a doctor. I accept the diploma, 'tis engraved on my back'. And so Sganarelle is introduced to Géronte as being an eminent and accomplished physician.

Géronte explains to Sganarelle that he is to examine and treat Lucinde, and if possible restore to her the lost faculty of speech. Sganarelle finds this to be a strange injunction: 'What a fool, to be sure, who would seek for a cure. Who would not leave a woman speechless? I have a wife sir, and on my life sir, I regret that my wife is not beset with this charming defect!' Nevertheless, the prospect of a fee causes Sganarelle to press on. Having ascertained that Géronte speaks no Latin, he impresses that gentleman by reeling off the Latin rigmarole that he once learned by rote. Then, after a lengthy, painstaking, and demonstrative examination of the patient, Sganarelle confirms that the correct diagnosis is indeed dumbness. 'What a wonderful doctor!' exclaim the spectators.

Sganarelle then more injudiciously informs Géronte that his daughter's illness is caused by certain noxious humours: 'The said vapours having passed from the left side (wherein is found the liver) to the right side (wherein is found the heart)'. Géronte raises an objection: 'Is not the heart on the left and the liver on the right?' Sganarelle's footwork is deft: 'Aha! 'Twas so in the old days, but now we ha' changed all that. Physick these days depends on principles entirely new'. Géronte retreats: 'I crave your pardon. Report had not reached me'.

Sganarelle's initial therapeutic recommendation is that the speechless daughter be fed 'a mess of bread well steeped in wine'. This is reasoned from his observation that parrots so nourished can often be induced to speak. Not surprisingly, however, this medication, whatever it might achieve for parrots, does not improve Lucinde's speech, and her father complains that if anything she is worse, and likely soon to be pickled. But Sganarelle is unabashed: 'Good! 'Tis a sign the cure is awork'.

The situation is then very markedly altered by the arrival of Lucinde's would-be lover, Léandre. There is hereabouts an initial slight misunderstanding. Léandre enters and addresses Sganarelle: 'Sir! I implore your assistance!' Sganarelle feels Léandre's pulse: 'A very ill pulse!' Léandre: 'I am not ill sir. 'Tis not for that I come'. Sganarelle: 'The devil! Why said you not so?'

Léandre explains that he is the suitor of Lucinde, but that her father refuses to allow the pair of them to meet. Léandre begs Sganarelle to facilitate for him an assignation with Lucinde. Sganarelle does not take kindly to this proposition: 'What do you take me for? You dare to so address me, to so traduce the dignity of a doctor by an employment of this nature?' Léandre: 'Sir, no noise!' Sgaranelle forces Léandre back: 'I desire to make noise, thou ill-advised oaf!' Léandre: 'Softly, sir!' Sganarelle: 'Thou scanderbeg! Be advised that I am no man for such a business, and rather [at this point Léandre draws out a purse and hands it to Sganarelle] I do not speak of you, for you are an honest soul; I am at your service'. Thus does the exchange of cash weaken resolve and induce fickleness. Léandre informs Sganarelle: 'Know then sir, that this malady you have been summoned to cure is a sham'. Sganarelle: 'I' faith, this Lucinde is not dumb? Well, young sir, you have inspired in me a tenderness for you love-birds. I shall aid you!'

Sganarelle, having thus adjusted his allegiance, prudently ascertains that

Léandre and the father Géronte have never met. Consequently emboldened, Sganarelle devises a further fraudulent scheme to outwit the father. Sganarelle compounds the deception on which he is already well embarked by having the suitor Léandre masquerade as his medical assistant. Sganarelle introduces that fake assistant to Géronte, and then directs his so-called auxiliary to take Lucinde for a walk in the garden 'to feel her pulse'. Meanwhile Sganarelle diverts the father's attention by gabbling medical nonsense to him.

When Lucinde and Léandre return from their stroll, Lucinde can once more speak. Géronte is initially overjoyed at Sganarelle's seemingly wondrous cure, but then he is less well pleased to have his daughter inform him that she will never wed anyone other than Léandre. Géronte turns on Sganarelle: 'Sir, I implore you, make her dumb again!' Sganarelle: 'Impossible, sir! But I can make you deaf'. Géronte declines this kindness with polite irony: 'I thank you'.

But then, when all seems destined to be lost in confusion, matters are resolved, once again in rather hackneyed operatic fashion. Léandre announces: 'I have but now received a letter which informs me that my uncle is dead and I his sole heir'. Géronte swiftly changes course: 'Sir, such virtue must be rewarded! I give you my daughter's hand with all the pleasure in the world!' And just as Géronte was about to have the fraudulent Sganarelle arrested by the constable, he relents.

Sganarelle returns to his wife Martine, and initially demands to be treated with the respect due to a physician of his eminence. However, Martine is having none of it, and has forestalled him by arranging for a chorus of woodcutters to threaten him with sticks, a scenario which can of course, readily be organized in opera. Sganarelle sensibly and swiftly changes his mind, and the opera ends with his words: 'Good friends, I have obtained license enough, and have this moment recalled that I am a woodbinder e'en as you'.

This is, I consider, a delightful comedy, with some sparkling music, and it is an opera which deserves more frequent productions than it receives. The passages of spoken dialogue especially require to convey the wit and humour of Molière's original play; hence in my opinion Herman and Apter were right to adopt 17th-century pastiche in their 1979 English translation of Barbier and Carré's libretto.

---

1. In 1768 Mesmer commissioned the 12-year-old Mozart's opera *Bastien und Bastienne*, which was first performed in his house in the Landstrasse district of Vienna.

30

ANOTHER MISTAKEN DIAGNOSIS

HANS WERNER HENZE: WE COME TO THE RIVER 1976

In opera, as in real life, mistaken diagnoses by doctors are not rare, with consequences ranging from comic to horrific. In Puccini's *Gianni Schicchi* (see Chapter 13) Dr Spinelloccio erroneously supposes old Buoso to be still alive although he is in fact dead, thus enabling Gianni Schicchi and the relatives to prepare a fraudulent will. In the several operatic versions of Edgar Allan Poe's tale *The Fall of the House of Usher* (see Chapter 26), the resident family doctor makes the converse error, pronouncing Madeline Usher dead while she is still alive, and so leading to her macabre emergence from her coffin several days later. The misdiagnosis in *We Come to the River* is of a very different kind, albeit the consequences are again disturbing.

In *We Come to the River* the librettist Edward Bond and the composer Hans Werner Henze unashamedly present full-scale political music theatre, wherein war is condemned by the oppressed, who are those who most suffer its consequences. A crucial aspect of Bond's libretto is the dramatic convention of blindness being a metaphor for insight, the reason why Oedipus, Tiresias, and again Gloucester in Shakespeare's *King Lear* are blind. Also made blind is Lear in Bond's own play of that name. Bond's Lear 'is blind until they take his eyes away, and by then he has begun to see, to understand'.

The central character in Henze's opera is the General, a baritone. As the work opens, a people's uprising in a province of the Empire has just been bloodily put down. The General dictates a dispatch to the Emperor; a deserter is condemned to death; victorious soldiers get drunk; and an official congratulatory reception is held.

Then the General is visited in his tent by the Doctor (bass-baritone). The Doctor informs the General that as a consequence of a leg wound sustained many years earlier he will, at some uncertain time in the future, go blind. Not unreasonably, the General is initially highly sceptical of this confident but improbable diagnosis, while the Doctor, albeit firm in his assertion, remains disturbingly evasive concerning the pathophysiology. Nevertheless, despite the General's well-founded doubts about the Doctor's expertise, he has inadvertently acquired worrying insight into his military actions and their consequences.

The General now perceives the suffering he has caused. He runs out to the battlefield; he hears the moaning of the wounded and dying; he meets a young woman (soprano) seeking the corpse of her husband (who is in fact not yet dead, but is the deserter who is about to be shot, on the General's own orders); he encounters other women scavenging the dead for saleable items. He becomes progressively preoccupied and disaffected and curses the regime which hitherto he has served loyally. The General and his voice become symbols of freedom and protest, and he is, although wholly compos mentis, eventually silenced by imprisonment in an asylum for the insane.

The political situation worsens, and the Emperor (mezzo-soprano 'trousers' role) now asks the General to resume military command, where his prestige would be invaluable. When the General refuses, his eyes are put out on the orders of the Emperor. Now truly physically blinded, although not by way of the pathology predicted by the Doctor, the General sees reality even more clearly.

The opera ends with the oppressed people singing of hope and a better future:

> We stand by the river.
> If there is no bridge we will wade.
> If the water is deep we swim.
> We will stand on the other side.
> We have learned to march so well that we cannot drown.

The critic Peter Heyworth wrote of this opera: 'Its first performance at Covent Garden will surely stand as a significant date in the annals of twentieth-century music theatre'.[1] The medical naiveté which so disturbs me went almost certainly unnoticed by the great majority of the audience. Once again I am reminded that over-familiarity with medical matters can impair musico-dramatic appreciation.

---

1.   Heyworth, P., *The Observer*, 18 July 1976.

31

DOCTORS AS POLITICIANS

I propose to consider now an activity taken up remarkably often by (usually lapsed) doctors, and which excites in their colleagues a strikingly wide range of emotions, from admiration and envy at one extreme through to alarm and anxiety at the other. That controversial pursuit is the doctor as politician. This is a calling which clearly has a strong appeal to medical men and women, and the political arena is littered with doctors having a variety of colours, political or cutaneous. The subsequent fortunes of such doctors have also been distinctly disparate, although it is by no means unusual for them to follow a course from medicine to politics to prison.

One such example is Dr Leander Starr Jameson. Jameson was born at Stranraer in south-west Scotland. He received his medical training at University College, London, then emigrated to South Africa and for a time practised medicine at Kimberley. He abandoned medicine for politics, and in December 1895 led the infamous Jameson Raid on the Transvaal. He was ignominiously captured by the Boers, returned to the British authorities, tried in London, and sentenced to fifteen months' imprisonment.

Dr Sun Yat-Sen, a medical graduate of Hong Kong, led uprisings against the Manchu emperors of China. Dr Sun was, on a visit to London in 1896, kidnapped and imprisoned in the Chinese legation. He was released and saved from almost certain death only through the intervention of Sir James Cantlie, the surgeon. Dr Sun Yat-Sen eventually prevailed; in 1912 China was proclaimed a republic, with him as its provisional president.

A particularly interesting instance is Dr Hastings Banda. He was born in what was then Nyasaland in Southern Africa, at a date which is uncertain, but seems to have been between 1898 and 1906. He studied first in South Africa, then in the USA, and obtained an American medical qualification. He came to Britain, acquiring the so-called triple medical qualification of the combined Glasgow and Edinburgh colleges. During the Second World War he practised medicine first in

Liverpool and then South Shields; after that war for a time in Renfrew and subsequently in London. He returned to Nyasaland in 1958 to become the political leader of the Malawi African Congress. In 1959 he was imprisoned for sedition, albeit later receiving an unconditional pardon. Nyasaland became the independent Republic of Malawi in 1964. The name 'Malawi' was seemingly invented by Hastings Banda, who liked the sound of the word. Hastings Banda became first the prime minister and then the president of Malawi, and established strict authoritarian one-party rule. He lost the presidency when multiple political parties were established in 1994, and was subsequently placed under house arrest and tried for alleged complicity, in the 1980s, in the murder of three cabinet ministers and another member of parliament. The murder of three cabinet ministers and another member of parliament is certainly a dramatic prospect. He was, however, found to be not guilty, and was acquitted. Hastings Banda died in 1997 at an age thought to be somewhere between ninety-one and ninety-nine years.

Among present-day medical men become politicians, and who have, so far at any rate, avoided the final translation to incarceration, we have David Owen (now Lord Owen), a graduate of Cambridge University and St Thomas' Hospital, London. David Owen has been, at different times in his career, a member of the Labour party, then a Social Democrat; currently he describes himself as a crossbencher. There is Sam Galbraith, Glasgow University, Labour; and Liam Fox, also Glasgow University, Conservative. Notable female doctor/politicians include Elizabeth Garrett Anderson and Edith Summerskill.

VERDI: THE SICILIAN VESPERS 1855

The first of the two operas I shall now consider is *The Sicilian Vespers* of 1855, which Verdi composed to a libretto in French by Scribe and Duveyrier. This opera *The Sicilian Vespers* is based on a real historical event, the uprising in the year 1282 of the Sicilians at Palermo against their French rulers, Sicily at that time being part of the empire of Charles, Count of Anjou and Provence, King of Sicily, Albania, and Jerusalem. The revolution was of great significance in European history, causing the collapse of the political if not the theological authority of the Pope and, according to the historian Steven Runciman, leading 'through schism and disillusion to the troubles of the Reformation'.[1]

The revolt was engineered by Dr John of Procida, a Salerno-born physician become intriguer and political agitator. In some accounts (there are many inconsistencies) Procida was yet another who followed the course from medicine to politics to prison. According to Edward Gibbon: 'His birth was noble, but his education [as a physician] was learned'.[2] The word 'but' there is a nice touch. Evidently in Gibbon's view nobility of birth and medical expertise were to be regarded as usually incongruous. Gibbon continues: 'He showed deviousness of a complexity extreme even by the Italian standards of the 13th century ... he persuaded each to whom he spoke that he laboured solely for their interest; that these assertions were incompatible one with another he concealed from his hearers one and all'. So, apparently, not much has changed in politics in the past 700-odd years. I am, however, not informed about what arrangements Dr Procida made concerning his expenses claims.

Verdi was commissioned to compose this work for the Paris Opéra of the day; therefore it had to be in five acts, and had to include a ballet. The libretto was to be by the ubiquitous Eugène Scribe. Scribe had written dozens of operatic libretti. His authorial technique can perhaps best be described as one of mechanical eclecticism. Originality of thought seems rarely, if ever, to have entered into the matter. A contemporary cartoon of Scribe at work shows behind him drawers labelled variously 'comic situations', 'dramatic situations', 'puns', 'witticisms', 'verses', 'endings', and so forth. It was held that Scribe simply took pre-cooked items from the appropriate compartments, mixed them together in some sort of order, and then served up the resulting concoction as a so-called libretto. What Verdi got from Scribe for *The Sicilian Vespers* was not even that, but basically an old text Scribe had earlier written for Donizetti (although later Verdi claimed not to know that at the time) and formerly entitled *The Duke of Alba*. That previous version dealt with an uprising in Flanders in the 16th century. So far as Scribe was concerned, one revolution was much the same as the next. For Verdi, Scribe simply altered the title, the names of the characters and some details of the plot, and then offered up that script for Verdi to set. The story remained in many aspects the same; much of the dialogue was quite unaltered. Remarkably, one Charles Duveyrier is credited as having assisted Scribe with the preparation of the libretto for Verdi, yet so little effort seems to have been put into the matter that it is difficult for me to see why two people were needed. Perhaps the presence of Duveyrier's name was intended to give the illusion of creative industry. Verdi wrote a long letter of complaint to Louis Crosnier, Director of the Paris Opéra, concerning the lassitude of Scribe, but to no effect.

Included at the centre of the plot is a routine device by Scribe, that of mistaken identity. Arrigo, tenor, leader of the planned Sicilian revolution, is, initially unknown to them both, the bastard son of the French governor of Sicily, the baritone Montforte. Dr Procida (bass) lands from exile to foment revolution in Sicily, and is welcomed at the beach by Arrigo and by Arrigo's beloved, the soprano Elena.

In the final scene of this long opera, Elena is about to be married to Arrigo. Dr Procida then reveals to Elena that the peals of the wedding bells will be the signal for church bells to ring throughout the town (this is 'The Sicilian Vespers' of the title) and at that sign the Sicilians will rise up against the French. Elena is aghast. She does not want this sort of thing going on at her wedding. She cannot however bring herself to denounce Procida, and so she simply refuses to go ahead with the ceremony but without giving any reason. There is general consternation. Montforte, now of course revealed as being Arrigo's father, arrives with knights and ladies. Montforte brushes aside Elena's objections, joins her hand to Arrigo's, and orders the wedding bells to be rung. Church bells then begin to peal throughout Palermo, armed Sicilians rush in from all sides shouting cries of vengeance, and the opera ends with the rebels hurling themselves homicidally on Montforte and the French.

Although Verdi's musical idiom was fundamentally unsuited to the rather overblown fashion of mid-19th-century Paris, the work does contain some admirable music. The opera survives mainly in its Italian version, and remains popular in Italy to this day. Remarkably, in 1855, the year of its composition, Sicily was once more under foreign rule, being then part of the Bourbon Kingdom of the Two Sicilies. Thus the plot of the opera offered distinct contemporary encouragement to Garibaldi and the Italian Risorgimento, the planned reunification of Italy. Even so, in the 19th century the work seems to have caused some political irritation all round. Many Italians, Garibaldi notwithstanding, were upset at being portrayed as villainous, cowardly and duplicitous; the French, more understandably, were resentful at seeing themselves massacred by Italians; and Austrians in Italy were alarmed at the idea of Italians rising up to expel an occupying power. Despite all that, *The Sicilian Vespers* achieved fifty performances at the Paris Opéra in its first season.

BO HOLTEN: THE VISIT OF THE ROYAL PHYSICIAN 2009
Like Dr John of Procida in Verdi's opera *The Sicilian Vespers*, the politically inclined doctor we shall now meet, Johann Friedrich Struensee, was a major participant in what were real historical events. These are recounted in Bo Holten's opera *The Visit of the Royal Physician*, which was composed to a libretto in Danish by Enquist after his own novel.

The 17-year-old King Christian VII, a tenor, has, in the year 1766, succeeded to the Danish throne. Surrounded by scheming courtiers, and supposed to be mentally feeble, he is compelled to marry the 15-year-old Caroline Mathilde, mezzo-soprano, sister to the British King George III. It is recommended that the inexperienced and wayward young King have a personal tutor and counsellor. The German doctor Johann Friedrich Struensee, baritone, is hence persuaded to leave his work with the poor of Altona, and is appointed Danish Royal Physician. Struensee is, although politically naive, a scholar and a student of the Enlightenment. He uses his considerable influence to curb and then reform the widespread abuses and corruption of the Danish court, the latter described by John Williams, an English visitor, as 'meant to be enlightened absolutism, but more like a badly managed poorhouse with an arbitrary system of justice and with laws that are turned ... in favour of the mighty ... it is hard to tell whether it is its wickedness or its stupidity that is most striking'.

King Christian is too fearful to approach his young wife's bed, and the services of a courtesan, 'Bootee-Caterine', soprano, are enlisted to initiate him into the world of eroticism. Meanwhile, the neglected young Queen Caroline Mathilde embarks on a love affair with Dr Struensee and becomes pregnant.

Formerly influential, now resentful, figures, curbed by Struensee's reforms and headed by King Christian's stepmother, the Queen Dowager Juliane Marie, soprano, seize power in a coup. Struensee is arrested and executed, Queen Caroline Mathilde is exiled, and their daughter Louise Augusta officially declared Princess, with King Christian VII as her nominal father. Louise Augusta is thus an ancestress of many of the European royal families of today.

The opera's composer, Holten, has explicitly employed diverse musical styles, including, as appropriate, 18th-century pastiche. He has taken great pains with the enunciation of the text, placing the most important details in the middle registers of the singers so as to facilitate clarity. This is, I consider, an opera of some distinction.

Because so many operatic doctors are presented as forbidding, ethically dubious, incompetent, or simply pretentious figures of fun, Struensee, idealistic but too trusting, should, I believe, be accorded an appropriate encomium. Another contemporary Englishman, Nathanael Wraxall, who interviewed the exiled Caroline Mathilde, wrote of him, 'As a statesman I account Struensee to be of the standing of Sir Thomas More, who also suffered an early and ignominious death, but who has been rehabilitated by the impartial judgement of posterity'.[3]

1. Sicilian Vespers. See Preface note 14, pp. 277–91.
2. Gibbon. See Preface note 21.
3. Quotations from booklet accompanying Dacapo DVD, 2010.

32

A VERY BRIEF AND OVER-OPTIMISTIC MEDICAL CLAIM

PROKOFIEV: THE FIERY ANGEL 1955

Prokofiev composed this opera to his own libretto, which he derived from the 1907 novel of the same title by Valery Bryusov. It should be noted that the opera was first performed in 1955, two years after Prokofiev's death; he never saw it on stage.

There has over the years been a good deal of light-hearted speculation concerning what is the shortest contribution by a named singing principal in opera. There are many possibilities particularly in 19th-century Italian operas, but a hot favourite for this distinction in the German repertoire is the baritone role of Der Steuermann (The Helmsman) in Wagner's *Tristan und Isolde*. *Tristan und Isolde* is a very long opera, and the demands made on the heldentenor performing Tristan, who has a lengthy participation in all three acts, are weighty. By contrast, Der Steuermann does not appear until the final scene of the entire opera, Scene 3 of Act III, when he rushes in and sings just four bars of music to the stirring words:

> We are outnumbered!
> Resistance is useless!

And with that rousing message he very sensibly, given the substance of his advice, leaves the stage for good. The part of the Doctor in *The Fiery Angel* is also very brief, but the import of what he has to communicate is, in contrast to Der Steuermann's near panic, complacently optimistic.

The central character in *The Fiery Angel* is the psychologically unbalanced Renata, a soprano. Since childhood she has been obsessed with her probably imagined protective fiery angel. The relationship was initially purely spiritual, but after puberty became physical. For a year she then lived with a Count Heinrich, a man she believed was the fiery angel of her childhood fantasies. It is far from clear that there is, or ever was, a fiery angel, even less that Count Heinrich is its incarnation. Not in doubt is that Count Heinrich, having for a year cohabited with Renata, then deserted her, and his desertion, hardly surprisingly, exacerbated her ravings. In the opera Count Heinrich has a silent role. Renata tells her troubles to the baritone Ruprecht after he has encountered her experiencing wild visions. Unlike almost everyone else, who regard Renata as either insane, or a witch, or both, Ruprecht, having fallen in love with Renata, agrees to help her.

In Act III Renata once more meets Count Heinrich, but yet again he rejects her. The scorned Renata then, in a traditional fury, persuades Ruprecht to challenge Count Heinrich to a duel. However, at the last crucial moment Renata changes her mind, and commands Ruprecht not to harm her 'fiery angel'. Hardly surprisingly Ruprecht, bewildered by these vacillating instructions, is badly wounded in the duel. Renata, now remorseful, vows to love Ruprecht and restore him to health. Voices are heard, mocking her promise. It is at this point that the Doctor, tenor, makes his blithe insouciant entry, and airily tries to reassure Renata by talking glibly of 'the omnipotence of medicine in this enlightened century'. As the date of the action is 1534, the Doctor's confident claims can, and almost certainly should, be taken with some reserve. They definitely, and for once sensibly, are discounted by Renata, who in a rare phase of lucidity takes on the nursing of Ruprecht herself and she is eventually successful in restoring him to health.

Comparisons between *The Fiery Angel* and Wagner's *Tristan und Isolde* are interesting. Prokofiev's Renata has, like the heldentenor Tristan, a most demanding operatic role; her recurrent hysterics obtrude in all but two scenes of the five-act opera. By contrast with Renata's test of endurance, the part of the Doctor in *The Fiery Angel*, although it is marginally longer than Der Steuermann's four bars, is slight; the Doctor sings for a total time of less than a minute at the conclusion of Act III. Hence, whereas there are often some anxieties as to whether Tristan or Renata will have the stamina to see things through, their respective confrères, Der Steuermann and the Doctor, face the converse problem of having insufficient time to develop their roles. I have often wondered what size of fee the latter pair command.

33

DOCTOR AS PHILANDERER

PAISIELLO: THE BARBER OF SEVILLE 1782
ROSSINI: THE BARBER OF SEVILLE 1816;
MOZART: THE MARRIAGE OF FIGARO 1786
DITTERSDORF: THE MARRIAGE OF FIGARO 1789
PORTUGAL: THE MARRIAGE OF FIGARO 1799

The French author Beaumarchais, who lived from 1732 to 1799, wrote, among many works, three plays which are centred on Count Almaviva and his family plus, of course, that man of many talents, Figaro. The three plays are *The Barber of Seville* (*Le barbière de Séville*) (1755), *The Marriage of Figaro* (*Le mariage de Figaro*) (1784), and *The Guilty Mother* (*La mère coupable*) (1797). All three have been set as operas: *The Barber of Seville* by Paisiello and by Rossini; *The Marriage of Figaro* by Mozart, by Dittersdorf, and by Portugal; and *The Guilty Mother* by Darius Milhaud. Of these operas, *The Barber of Seville*, in Paisiello's version to a libretto by Petrosellini and in Rossini's version to a libretto by Sterbini; and Mozart's *The Marriage of Figaro* to a libretto by Da Ponte, are those that principally concern us here. Dittersdorf's *The Marriage of Figaro* seems sadly to have been lost. Portugal's version was successfully revived by Bampton Classical Opera in 2010.

Beaumarchais was a colourful figure, possessing diverse talents additional to his literary proficiency. As well as being an author he was at various times clockmaker, libertine, adventurer, financial speculator, music-teacher, intriguer, jailbird, gun-runner, and spy. The character Figaro is supposed to epitomize all the skills and vices of the author who created him. So we are to see Figaro at least to an extent as Beaumarchais himself.

When we first meet Figaro, a baritone, in (and as) *The Barber of Seville*, he is already in his twenties. He is unscrupulous, witty, and with a wide range of accomplishments, some of which are distinctly dubious. Figaro's adversary, Dr Bartolo (bass), is a busy, and evidently prosperous, general practitioner. Requiring emphasis is that such is Dr Bartolo's profession. It is often, but wrongly, supposed that he is a lawyer, but Beaumarchais clearly has him as 'a physician from Seville'.[1] Dr Bartolo possesses forceful and somewhat reactionary views. He is antipathetic towards democracy and freedom of thought; he dislikes contemporary drama; scientifically he expresses disbelief in gravity, electricity and magnetism; medically, he is sceptical of inoculation and of the value of quinine in treating malaria. Most importantly Bartolo and Figaro are mutually antagonistic, and this is a situation already seemingly of some duration. The character Marcellina, whom we shall meet in *The Marriage of Figaro*, does not appear on stage in *The Barber of Seville*, although she is several times alluded to. We learn in *The Barber of Seville* (albeit the wording is rather vague) that she is unwell, and that she is being attended by Dr Bartolo. This is a circumstance which, in the light of later information, could attract unwelcome attention from the General Medical Council (that is, if there were such an organisation in Spain in the 18th century, which probably there was not). Dr Bartolo has a ward, Rosina, an orphan of noble birth and who is seemingly wealthy. Rosina is a soprano in Paisiello's opera; a mezzo-soprano in that of Rossini. Dr Bartolo wishes to make Rosina his wife, but in this he is thwarted by the machinations of his adversary Figaro, and Rosina instead becomes wedded to Count Almaviva (tenor), the Count having been greatly helped in his wooing by Figaro. Hence the enmity between Dr Bartolo and Figaro, already distinct, is inevitably much worsened.

The sequel, *The Marriage of Figaro*, the action of which takes place some three years later, is dramatically much darker. The union between Count Almaviva (here a baritone) and Rosina (soprano) has soured, and the Count is philandering widely. In particular, his current target is Susanna (soprano), the fiancée of Figaro (baritone), Figaro now being employed as the Count's valet. In *The Barber* the Count and Figaro were allies. Here, although nominally master and servant, they are effectively in opposition. We learn in the course of this second drama that Figaro is now 30 years old. Marcellina, a soprano, now does appear in person, currently being housekeeper at the castle of Count Almaviva.

Dr Bartolo is summoned to the castle. At first he supposes that he is required to attend medically to the Count (a brief passage of the play omitted by Da Ponte), but he has in fact been invited so as to advise Marcellina in a lawsuit. Marcellina has made to Figaro a loan which he cannot repay, and the contract states that in default of payment Figaro must marry Marcellina. This he is reluctant to do. In the first place he does not particularly fancy Marcellina, who appears to him to be old enough to be his mother. And then, of course, there is the question of Figaro's betrothal to Susanna.

When the case comes to be heard before the Count, Figaro announces that he can not be married to Marcellina without the consent of his parents. He claims to be of noble birth, stolen by gypsies from his cot. His parents are unknown to him, but he does have a distinctive birth mark on his arm. This mark he is now asked to show, and it is at once recognised by Marcellina, who thus identifies

Figaro, her prospective husband, as in reality her own long-lost illegitimate son Emanuel (he is at any rate Emanuel in Beaumarchais' play; for some reason Da Ponte, in the opera libretto, has him as Raffaello).

Even more intriguingly, Dr Bartolo, Figaro's old enemy, turns out to be his natural father. To quote Shakespeare: 'It is a wise father that knows his own child'. The two parents, Bartolo and Marcellina, belatedly agree to wed, and Marcellina cancels Figaro's debt as a wedding gift to her newly rediscovered son.

So this part of the story turns out well, although were the members of the disciplinary committee of the General Medical Council to hear Marcellina's account of her seduction by Bartolo, this being another and lengthier passage which appears in Beaumarchais' play but which Da Ponte excised from the opera libretto, they could well be displeased. The General Medical Council does not look favourably upon doctors who have love affairs with patients. Of course, it is by no means clear that Bartolo was Marcellina's doctor when Figaro was conceived.

---

1. Beaumarchais, P., *The Barber of Seville* and *The Marriage of Figaro*. Translated by J. Wood. Penguin Books, London, 1964.

34

A WIFE MISTAKEN
FOR A HAT

MICHAEL NYMAN: THE MAN WHO MISTOOK HIS WIFE FOR A HAT 1986

This opera, to a libretto by Christopher Rawlence is, I believe, unique, in that it is throughout concerned exclusively with medicine; first the diagnosis, then the treatment, of an initially baffling neurological disorder. The title could imply flippancy, but any such impression would be misleading. This is a serious opera, and the title is wholly apposite. The music is, in this work, unusually and particularly integral to the plot.

The opera, which is taken straight through in just one act lasting for an hour, has a small chamber orchestra comprising two violins, a viola, two cellos, a harp, and a piano. There is a cast of three singers: Dr S., the neurological specialist (tenor); Mr P., the patient, a distinguished professional singer of classical music (baritone); and Mrs P., the patient's wife (soprano). Sometimes the patient is referred to as 'Dr P.' because he has a doctorate in music, but to avoid confusion I shall here refer to him as 'Mr P.' throughout. Dr Oliver Sacks, upon whose case report the opera is based,[1] is a New York physician specialising in diseases of the nervous system. He has written extensively on the manner in which some of these afflictions can alter musical appreciation and execution. He has also studied the therapeutic benefits of music in certain neurological disorders.

As the opera begins, the medical opinion of Dr S. is being sought because of some behavioural peculiarities developed by Mr P. For example, sometimes one of his singing students will present himself, and Mr P. does not recognise him or, more accurately, is not able to recognise his face. The moment the student speaks, however, Mr P. can identify him by the sound of his voice. Such incidents have recently multiplied, causing embarrassment, perplexity, and sometimes comedy. On an occasion when Mr P. got lost on his way to a concert he found himself unable to interpret a street map. He then asked a parking meter to direct him. The meter remained silent, so he proceeded to address a pillar box and attempted to discuss matters with that structure. Nevertheless, Mr P. shows no evidence of dementia, and his professional performances at concerts are unaffected.

Dr S. can find no specific abnormality on his initial examination of Mr P. Most importantly, so far as the doctor can ascertain, the patient's eyesight is unimpaired. Yet the doctor comments:

> He faced me as he spoke,
> Yet he looked at me with his ears,
> Not with his eyes.

Then, as the patient and his wife are leaving, and Mrs P. guides her husband towards the hat rack, he reaches out for her head, mistaking it for his hat. Dr S. is now seriously concerned:

> How could a professional musician,
> A practising teacher,
> Mistake his wife for a hat?

Dr S. decides to see Mr P. again, at the latter's own home. When the doctor arrives, he observes that Mr P. recognises him by the sound of his voice, not from his visual appearance. In short, further examination reveals that the patient has a rare neurological disorder, visual agnosia, a consequence of damage to the parts of the brain responsible for the interpretation of visual stimuli. He can see, but is unable to recognise, or to find sense in, what he sees. An analogy from another sensory system would be of someone hearing a foreign language of which he knows nothing. The spoken sounds can clearly be made out, yet they convey no sense to the listener. The patient is shown a rose. He describes what he sees in these terms:

> Six inches in length,
> Convoluted red form,
> With a linear green attachment.

Yet these observations, factually correct, transmit nothing coherent to him. He identifies the object as a rose only when he is asked to smell it.

It eventually emerges that Mrs P. is aware of her husband's disabilities, although she had at first denied it, and that she has developed an elaborate system in order to enable him to get by. She lays out his clothes, his food, and his washing things in a pattern they both know, and which he can follow. Further, Mr P. has come to employ what can be called an 'inner soundtrack', usually hummed tunes of one of his favourite composers, Schumann, to help him coordinate simple everyday tasks such as eating a meal, which, with his inability to make cognitive visual judgement, would otherwise be almost impossible for him. In the opera Mr P. sings part of

Schumann's song cycle *Dichterliebe* accompanied by his wife at the piano. Appropriately, the song is 'Ich grolle nicht' ('I won't complain, even though my heart may break'). After the song, both the doctor and the patient's wife comment:

> He still has a perfect ear!
> Perfect tonal and rhythmic discrimination and expression!

The doctor can offer only limited, but nonetheless most valuable, therapeutic advice. Mr P. is encouraged by Dr S. to cultivate even more the coherence that, as he has already discovered for himself, music can provide, and to utilise those talents to the utmost.

Dr S. concludes the opera, and the story, with these words:

> I think that music, for him,
> Took the place of the image.
> He had no body image,
> He had body music.
> And to this inner soundtrack,
> He moved and he acted
> Fluently, cogently.
> But ... when the music ...
> Stopped, so did he ...

---

1. Sacks, O., *The Man who Mistook his Wife for a Hat*, Picador, London, 1986.

35

A GENERAL PRACTITIONER'S NIGHTMARE

HANS WERNER HENZE: A COUNTRY DOCTOR 1951

Starkly contrasted with the gentle fantasies induced in *Dream Angus*, discussed in Chapter 12, is the nightmare of *A Country Doctor*, composed by Henze to a libretto derived from Kafka. This is a one-act opera of unrelieved horror. When the work was presented at the St Pancras Festival in 1966 the set designs, by Helen Spankie, were, at the composer's recommendation, in the style of Edvard Munch.

On a winter's night, in a blizzard, the Doctor (baritone) is summoned urgently to a sick child 10 miles away. An unknown stable-boy arrives mysteriously with two strange horses, harnesses them to the Doctor's carriage and hustles the Doctor away. As he leaves, the horrified physician sees the boy attempting to rape his servant-girl.

The Doctor is welcomed by the parents of the ill child, who begs however to be allowed to die. Yet the Doctor can initially detect no medical abnormality. Suddenly the horses mysteriously break free and thrust their heads through the window into the room. The Doctor is about to depart when the parents beg him to examine the patient again. He now finds a dreadful wound in the boy's side, bleeding and crawling with worms. Then strangers enter the room, undress the Doctor, and put him into bed with the diseased child.

The Doctor decides to escape, jumps from the bed, gathers his clothes without putting them on, rushes out, and leaps into his carriage. Now, however, the horses will move only very slowly and circuitously. His route is lined by jeering patients, not one of whom will help him to dress. He returns home to find the stable-boy now ruling in his house.

The Doctor recognises all these dreadful events as an unreal nightmare, yet he is unable to awaken from it; he cannot escape the scarcely tolerable sense of having perpetrated a terrible medical error with the consequent ruin of his practice.

36

ECCENTRICITY, RABIES, AND POSSESSION BY THE DEVIL

PÉTER EÖTVÖS: LOVE AND OTHER DEMONS 2008

The opera *Love and Other Demons* is by the Hungarian composer Péter Eötvös to a libretto by Kornél Hamvai after the 1994 novel *Of Love and Other Demons* by Gabriel Garcia Márquez. This opera, first performed in 2008, offers eccentricity, rabies, and possession by the Devil. What more could one want? There is, nevertheless, a good deal more.

The action takes place around the year 1750 in the town of Cartagena, on the Caribbean coast of what was then the Spanish colony of Colombia. The central figure in the drama is the 12-year-old Siervia Maria de Todos los Angeles, sung by a soprano in the opera. Siervia Maria is the daughter of the languid 2nd Marquis de Casalduero, Don Ygnacio (tenor). Don Ygnacio is described by the writer Márquez as 'pale, ... funereal and effeminate'.[1]

Siervia Maria's mother, Bernarda Cabrera, is, in the original novel, eccentric to the point of madness, and addicted to purgatives, which cause her to 'break wind in pestilential explosions which startle the mastiffs'. The mother does not appear in the opera, and is assumed to be dead. One reason for her exclusion by the librettist was no doubt the difficulty in reproducing the appropriate acoustic effects on stage.

At any rate, the daughter, the young Siervia Maria, is effectively almost wholly lacking in parental care, brought up by slaves and servants, and speaking, in addition to Spanish, various African languages acquired from those slaves, among whom she has spent most of her time, and from whom she has also learnt native dances. Importantly therefore, Siervia Maria is very different in behaviour, linguistic accomplishments and predilections from what might be expected in a child of an aristocratic Spanish colonial family. Those peculiarities of character in the young Siervia Maria are, as we shall see, to have unhappy consequences for her.

On her twelfth birthday Siervia Maria is taken by a servant, Dominga, to the market used by the African slaves. Dominga is, in the opera, appropriately sung by a black mezzo-soprano. There then occur two crucial events; there is an eclipse of the sun, and Siervia Maria is bitten by a dog which is subsequently found to be infected with rabies. The coincidence of the dog bite with the solar eclipse is taken to be particularly ominous.

Siervia Maria's father, the Marquis Don Ygnacio, learns of her bite by the rabid dog, and is sufficiently concerned to rouse himself from his torpor and seek the advice of Dr Abrenuncio (tenor). Dr Abrenuncio is a Sephardic Jew, who has been persecuted and hounded from his native Portugal. There is also much antipathy towards him in Cartagena. Particularly adverse is a rumour that he once raised a patient from the dead. This seems to me to constitute an especially inapt criticism, even were it true, given the much-lauded Christian raising of Lazarus. Moreover, if that were correct, it would comprise a substantial therapeutic achievement by Dr Abrenuncio. Nevertheless, it is held against him. Dr Abrenuncio examines Siervia Maria. He notes that the dog bite was on the ankle; hence if she is to develop rabies there will first be a lengthy period of uncertainty, as the incubation time is longer the further the initial wound is from the brain. The rabies virus must traverse the peripheral nerves and reach the brain before symptoms appear. Nevertheless, his opinion is that Siervia Maria will probably not develop rabies. If, however, she does, there is unfortunately no known effective remedy. This calm, considered evaluation by the doctor, and his careful measured prognosis constitute one of the few rational episodes in an opera in which most of the other characters usually exhibit wildly inappropriate and excited overactivity. The Marquis nobly announces that if Siervia does develop rabies, he will ensure that her last days, however horrible, will be at home under his supervision and care.

However, there then occurs a complication not foreseen by the Marquis. The Bishop (bass) has heard of Siervia Maria's possible illness. He is also aware that she often speaks in various incomprehensible tongues, and that she engages in wild pagan dances with African slaves. This latter behaviour the Bishop interprets as evidence that Siervia is possessed by the Devil. The Bishop dismisses the notion that Siervia may be incubating rabies: 'One of the Devil's numerous deceptions is to take on the appearance of a foul disease in order to enter an innocent body'. The Bishop instructs that Siervia Maria be sent to the Convent of Santa Clara so that exorcism can be undertaken, and there, at the convent, to be under the orders of the Abbess Josefa (mezzo-soprano). Incidentally, this enables the Bishop to inconvenience the Abbess, with whom he has a long-standing feud.

Despite her violent protests, Siervia Maria is dressed in her long-dead grandmother's finery, which is considered to be appropriate for her admission to the convent. There another mishap befalls. Siervia Maria in her cell at the convent is befriended and cared for by Martina Laborde (mezzo-soprano), a former nun who really is insane, and who has been imprisoned for the apparently motiveless murder of two other nuns with a carving knife. The mad Martina tells Siervia Maria she should ask her demons to fly her out of the convent, because no one else will help her. This advice is wildly deranged and frighteningly impractical. To pursue a gambling metaphor, the young Siervia Maria really has been dealt a rotten hand.

But the malignant dealer has not yet finished with Siervia Maria. Her exorcism is assigned to one Father Delaura (baritone), the librarian of the Bishop. Unfortunately, Father Delaura falls in love with Siervia Maria, confesses his weakness to the Bishop, and is dismissed. The Bishop then undertakes the exorcism himself. The Bishop will be, we assume, and he hopes, immune to Siervia Maria's charms.

Hardly surprisingly, the ill-disciplined multilingual Siervia Maria reacts badly to these events, screaming and shouting in various languages, and resisting every attempt to restrain her. All of this unfortunately reinforces the prejudice that she is indeed the victim of demonic possession; the greater her physical violence and linguistic excess, the more convincing is held to be the evidence of the tenacity of the Devil in her case.

And then, catastrophically, as the Bishop determinedly pursues the exorcism, Siervia Maria suffers a convulsion and dies. Whether this is a consequence of rabies or otherwise is left unclear. In her final hours she could be exhibiting signs and symptoms of rabies, but more probably her excited ravings result from her maltreatment by the Bishop and the Abbess. What is certainly true is that Dr Abrenuncio's counsel was the soundest the poor girl was ever to receive. Dr Abrenuncio, though his advice was largely ignored, has to be numbered among the few commendable operatic doctors.

That, then, is a brief outline of this tale. The opera was, at its premiere performances at Glyndebourne in the summer of 2008, generally well-received. In the opera the conflicting cultures are skilfully evoked musically by the presence of three clearly different styles in the score. Linguistically, although English predominates in the libretto, Spanish and Yoruba also appear, emphasising the polyglot proclivities of Siervia Maria.

The story and the opera are however (according to the dramaturge Edward Kemp) intended to communicate also at another level. They could be interpreted as satirising present-day prejudices and the rigidity of the attitudes of different groups of people with opposing views. Some persons regard the opinions of those who are convinced of the reality of anthropogenic global warming as evincing gullibility and that such concerns replicate 18th-century fears of possession by the Devil. In that connection I have wondered sometimes if the composer, librettist, and dramaturge reflected on the piquancy in the Foreword to the Glyndebourne 2008 Programme Book, in which the Festival's Executive Chairman, Gus Christie, spoke of his aspirations to reduce carbon dioxide emissions by planning to erect a wind turbine near to the Opera House, and enjoined the audience to minimise Glyndebourne's 'carbon footprint', as he called it, by travelling to performances by train. Since then he has also forbidden helicopters to land at Glyndebourne. I very much regret, however, that I am unaware of what the creators of the opera thought of Gus Christie's schemes or of the viewpoint of dissenters.

1. The translations, from the original novel, are by Edith Grossman.

37

TWO DOWNTRODDEN PERSONAL PHYSICIANS

Nowadays only the rich and famous can aspire to a personal physician. The relationship between such a personal doctor and his patron is very different from that existing in many other circumstances. Traditionally it is the doctor who browbeats the patient; that situation is reversed in the case of a personal doctor.

HANS WERNER HENZE: ELEGY FOR YOUNG LOVERS 1961

Henze's opera *Elegy for Young Lovers* enjoyed a distinct vogue some 50 years ago. A German translation of Auden and Kallman's English libretto was undertaken by Ludwig Landgraf (pen-name of the Prince of Hesse) for the distinguished baritone Dietrich Fischer-Dieskau to perform the leading role of the poet Mittenhofer at the Schwetzingen premiere in 1961. The opera was then put on in its original English at the Glyndebourne Festival later that year. In 1970 Scottish Opera mounted, also in English, a much-lauded production by Henze himself to designs by Ralph Koltai and conducted by Alexander Gibson, with John Shirley-Quirk as the vainglorious writer Mittenhofer. Surprisingly, the work thereafter lapsed into some obscurity, from which it was rescued in 2010 by a new collaborative venture between English National Opera (ENO) and the Young Vic.

The satirical dramatic pivot of the action is the poet Mittenhofer, a figure explicitly created as a depiction of the now supposedly discredited 19th-century concept of artist as hero, to whom all others must be subservient. Mittenhofer's personal physician, the baritone Dr Reischmann, is, indisputably, submissive.

The action takes place in the year 1910 in an hotel, Der Schwartze Adler, in the Austrian Alps in the shadow of the Hammerhorn mountain. Koltai's mountain for Scottish Opera was a tubular structure, reminiscent of his famous 1960s designs for the ENO/Goodall/Wagner *Ring*. It was said that Koltai constructed the mountain for Scottish Opera out of the bits left over from *The Ring*.

Mittenhofer arrogantly assumes the role of artistic genius, and exploits ruthlessly all those around him. The deranged ravings of the widow Hilda Mack (soprano), whose husband was lost on the mountain during their honeymoon forty years earlier, Mittenhofer plunders heartlessly, utilising her fantasies as material for his writings. The Countess von Kirchstetten (contralto) acts as Mittenhofer's much-chastised secretary as well as being his very generous financial sponsor. The obsequious Dr Reischmann is obliged to provide for Mittenhofer supposedly rejuvenating injections on demand, and has also to resuscitate the hysterical victims of the poet's bullying. Obsequious Dr Reischmann may be, but there have been some noted exponents of that role. Thomas Hemsley was one such distinguished singer to have played Dr Reischmann; Thomas Hemsley also has recorded the part.

But then Mittenhofer finds that matters do not always go his way. His young mistress Elizabeth (soprano) falls in love with the doctor's son Toni. Toni, being an operatic lover, is of course by obligation a tenor. When Mittenhofer is made aware by the Countess of the young couple's clearly expressed love for each other he first plays on Elizabeth's feelings of guilt. Then he changes tack, and requests the doctor to bless the young pair.

Spitefully, notwithstanding a well-advertised impending storm, Mittenhofer asks the loving couple to venture out on to the mountain and to find for him a sprig of edelweiss which, for urgently compelling artistic reasons, he needs so as to complete a poem. However, once they have left, his mood veers from apparent acceptance to furious rage. When, predictably, Toni and Elizabeth are killed on the mountain, Mittenhofer shamelessly exploits the dual tragedy and writes, clearly for his own professional aggrandisement, a valedictory work, *Elegy for Young Lovers*. At the end of the opera Mittenhofer is seen complacently rehearsing that poem for a public reading in Vienna.

Interesting critical comparisons were made of two of the notable early singers portraying Mittenhofer: Dietrich Fischer-Dieskau aggressively overbearing; John Shirley-Quirk more crotchety and dessicated as that manipulative evil genius. One commentator, Conrad Wilson, considered both interpretations to be apt for each of two different productions: 'German is a more impressive language to be angry in than English ... Shirley-Quirk [in English] was better at capturing the half-tones of his part than the big outbursts'.[1] Dr Reischmann, a downtrodden weakling, is not, I have to concede, one of the more estimable of operatic doctors.

A few words concerning the 1961 Glyndebourne production of *Elegy for Young Lovers*, the first to be given using the original English libretto, may be of some interest. John Christie, the founder of the Glyndebourne Festival, was in charge at that time. John Christie was distinctly eccentric, and among many of his strong views (some would say bigoted views) was marked homophobia.[2] Bear in mind that society in general was then much less liberal than it is today; also that male homosexuality was still illegal in Britain.

John Christie had already, predictably, taken against Benjamin Britten and Peter Pears when *The Rape of Lucretia* was given at Glyndebourne in 1946. The following year, at the premiere performances of Britten's *Albert Herring*, Christie, clad allegedly sometimes in lederhosen and tennis shoes, was disposed to greet audience members on their arrival at Glyndebourne with the gloomy news: 'This isn't our sort of thing, you know'.

Hardly surprisingly, John Christie did not wholly welcome *Elegy for Young Lovers*, of which the composer, Henze, and both librettists, Kallman and Auden, were openly homosexual. Christie is said to have expressed his displeasure by stomping around talking loudly of his 'Allergy to old buggers'. That 1961 Glyndebourne production was further blighted by marked hostility on the part of the producer, Günther Rennert, towards the librettist Auden. Rennert then undermined the morale of the cast by declaring that scenes 7 and 8 of Act III were unperformable, and he excised them. John Christie gleefully claimed that a member of the audience had been overheard saying during the interval: 'We must warn poor Gwendoline'. Happily, no such misfortunes afflicted Scottish Opera's production nine years later, not at least so far as I am aware.

SALLY BEAMISH: MONSTER 2002

Sally Beamish composed *Monster* to a libretto by Janice Galloway. In that opera Lord Byron, baritone, has a personal physician, Dr Polidori, tenor, albeit the doctor makes almost no contribution to the musico-dramatic action. Dr Polidori does, however, like Dr Reischmann, have to endure repeated insults from his patron.

The more interesting research physician Dr Frankpierre of this opera is discussed in some detail in Chapter 20.

1. Wilson, C., *Scottish Opera: The First Ten Years*, Collins, Glasgow, 1972, pp: 144–9.
2. John Christie. See Preface note 18, passim.

Parsifal: The ailing Amfortas (Matthew Best) about to receive a healing jab from the now fully trained paramedic Parsifal (John Murray). Gurnemanz (Manfred Hemm) looks on anxiously. Scottish Opera, 2000. Photo: Bill Cooper.

38

THE ADMINISTRATOR AND THE WAITING LIST

WAGNER: PARSIFAL 1882

In none of Wagner's thirteen operas, all of them long, and some of them very long, is there a doctor. Nevertheless Wagner, although he provides no doctors for their care, has in those operas numerous characters in pressing need of medical attention. I propose now to examine just one of these medical situations, concerning an administrator and a waiting list. The work is Wagner's last, *Parsifal*, which he completed in 1882, the music therein, as always, set to his own text. The situation in *Parsifal* raises, as we shall see, two questions:

1. Should senior executives receive preferential treatment?
2. Is there a justifiable place for private medical care?

Amfortas (baritone) is ruler of the Brotherhood of the Knights of the Grail. But he, and hence the Brotherhood, are in serious trouble. Amfortas has been enticed into spending an illicit hour with the harlot Kundry (soprano), as a consequence of which he has acquired an especially unpleasant form of venereal disease. He has been beaten up by her pimp, Klingsor (bass), and Klingsor has stolen from him a spear sacred to the Knights of the Grail. This sacred spear is that with which the Roman soldier Longinus stabbed Christ on the Cross. Klingsor has wounded Amfortas with the stolen spear, and the wound will not heal. Hence at this point, in Act I, Amfortas has at least four major problems:

1. He has contracted venereal disease;
2. He has lost the holy spear;
3. He has been wounded by that spear, and the wound will not heal;
4. As a consequence of these several misfortunes his prestige and authority have been eroded, and the morale of the Knights is low.

The ailing Amfortas spends most of the time recumbent (in many productions on a trolley), accompanied by several medical attendants. Appropriately, Amfortas applies to have medical treatment, his application being submitted to a person we assume to be a very senior medical administrator, a person simply alluded to in the opera as 'The Almighty One'. Typically, Amfortas receives from the medical administrator an evasive and unsatisfactory reply. As Amfortas relates to one of his Knights, Gurnemanz (bass), on his return from his interview: 'I have to await the one appointed to me. I was told he is an innocent fool. Would that I were dead'. That at any rate is my rather free translation of Wagner's somewhat flowery romantic text: 'Ich harre des, der mir beschieden ... 'Der Reine Tor' ... dürft' ich den Tod ihn nennen!'

Amfortas' anxiety and displeasure at this news is understandable. A photograph taken at the Bayreuth premiere of the opera in 1882 shows the 'innocent fool', the tenor Parsifal (for it is he), undergoing his early paramedical training, and his aspect is not such as to inspire confidence in a prospective patient. So Amfortas settles down on his trolley for his long wait. And it is indeed a very long wait. In the libretto it is stated as being 'many years', remarkably similar to waiting times in the National Health Service. Even played live in the theatre the duration is of several hours.

But then we come at last to Act III, and Parsifal has completed his paramedical training. There is now a striking improvement in Parsifal's aspect. He is at this juncture brimming with confidence, often even smugness. Parsifal has also, in Act II, managed to retrieve the stolen sacred spear. Meanwhile, the condition of Amfortas has deteriorated alarmingly. In most productions Amfortas is by now unable even to have his soiled dressings changed regularly.

But all that is, at the hands of Parsifal, about to alter. Amfortas receives a symbolic injection of antibiotic via the holy spear, as Parsifal announces: 'Only the spear that smote you can heal your wound. Be whole, absolved, and atoned!' And the wound, as well as his venereal disease, is cured.

So finally, we must return to the questions posed. Should Amfortas have had to wait so long for treatment? Theatrically, dramatically of course, the answer is 'yes', otherwise we would not have the opera, with its sublime music. In real life, although the matter can be argued, the situation should, I think, be approached differently. Someone as important politically as Amfortas should be hurried up the queue, and/or be given access to private medical care. But all that, I have to recognise, is subject to what are no doubt very honest, yet conflicting, opinions.

39

A CANCER THERAPIST AND THE CONSEQUENCES OF INADEQUATE MEDICATION

POULENC: DIALOGUES DES CARMÉLITES 1957

A cancer specialist or oncologist is a doctor whose field is the treatment of malignant disease. A much-disputed issue which frequently faces such physicians nowadays is how to deal with a patient suffering terminal incurable cancer and in pain. There are those who hold, and I am one of their number, that in such circumstances it is crucial to administer a dose of drug sufficient to relieve discomfort, even if the large quantity taken might hasten death. There are others who, no doubt honestly, dissent from that view, and who would administer pain-relieving medicines more cautiously. A doctor who did, through giving heavy dosage, speed the death of his patient, could be criticised or even disciplined. This, precisely, is the pivotal issue in Poulenc's opera of 1957, *Dialogues des Carmélites*, composed to his own libretto after the play by Georges Bernanos. The doctor's action concerning just such a point determines the evolution of the plot.

The story centres on a convent of Carmelite nuns during the French Revolution, the nuns being for their religious faith persecuted by the revolutionaries, and is based on the actual memoirs of one of them, Mother Marie (mezzo-soprano), who by remarkable luck survived those events and lived until 1836. The Prioress of the Convent, Madame de Croissy (mezzo-soprano), is dying of what is presumed to be cancer. She begs her physician, Dr Javelinot (baritone), to give her sufficient medicine to relieve her pain. He, concerned that she has already received the maximum recommended dose, refuses to administer more.

In consequence, the Prioress dies in great distress, delirious, and uttering what are seemingly heretical words. This disturbing scene is witnessed by Blanche de la Force (soprano), a young nun, who as a result loses her faith and deserts the order. Blanche returns only at the very end of the opera, to rejoin her sister nuns on the scaffold when they have been condemned to the guillotine by revolutionaries.

The final scene is musically and theatrically one of the most vivid in all opera. The intermittent swish of the guillotine blade has been entered by Poulenc into the musical score. The condemned nuns, in chorus, sing 'Salve Regina', and ascend the scaffold one by one to be beheaded, their voices thus becoming progressively fewer as the executions proceed. Blanche, her faith now restored, is the last to be executed; as the blade falls for the final time her singing, all the singing, abruptly stops.

From the medical aspect, it is truly remarkable how a story dealing with the events of more than 200 years ago turns on a much argued and still unresolved therapeutic problem.

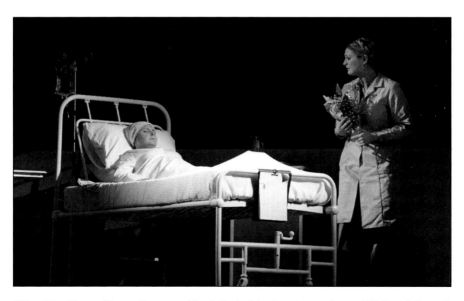

White: The Cleaner (Emma Carrington) by the bed of the dying Patient (Mary O'Sullivan). Scottish Opera, 2009. Photo: Richard Campbell.

A HOSPITAL DEATH

GARETH WILLIAMS: WHITE 2009

The librettist of Gareth Williams' one-act opera *White* is Margaret McCartney, a Glasgow doctor. She thus joins a very select group of physicians, which includes George Crabbe and Georg Büchner, who have provided either definitive operatic texts or the literary basis of those libretti.

This poignant drama was one of Scottish Opera's 2009 *Five:15 Operas Made in Scotland* group. The doctors and nurses here are silent but omnipresent, and provide a suitably sombre ambience. The very brief story is of a foreign hospital Cleaner (contralto), learning English by eavesdropping on the Mother (mezzo-soprano) comforting her dying daughter the Patient (soprano). When the Mother tries to reassure her daughter that she will see another summer, the Cleaner is sufficiently percipient to echo compassionately those sad but deceitful words.

Yet as the daughter dies, the doctors and nurses brusquely push the Cleaner aside in their vain attempts at resuscitation. The opera ends with the Mother and the Cleaner together singing mournfully: 'Dust spins dust, reflecting on us, dust'.

The harrowing central drama of the Mother and daughter, despite its poignancy, is almost commonplace. Yet the construction of the libretto is supremely accomplished. The involvement of the Cleaner adds a crucial dimension which enables the composer to convey a vivid musical drama within a brief 15 minutes.

AN IMPRUDENT
GENERAL
PRACTITIONER

Shakespeare's play *The Merry Wives of Windsor* is not one of his most accomplished or highly regarded plays, although it has attracted repeated attention from librettists as providing rewarding material for an operatic plot. Composers who have based operas on the play include Dittersdorf (1796), Salieri (1799), Balfe (1838), Adam (1856), and Vaughan Williams (1929). Probably the best known of the versions other than Verdi's is Nicolai's *Die Lustigen Weiber von Windsor* of 1849 in which the general practitioner Dr Caius is sung by a baritone. Verdi's *Falstaff* of 1893, in my opinion one of the most finely wrought operas ever, has Dr Caius as a tenor.

VERDI: FALSTAFF 1893

Verdi's opera, to a libretto by Boito, has no formal overture; it begins abruptly with Dr Caius, suffering a raging hangover, arriving at the Garter Inn in Windsor, where Falstaff is resident, and demanding an audience with him. On the previous evening Sir John Falstaff (baritone) and his henchmen, Bardolph (tenor) and Pistol (bass), had got Dr Caius very drunk, and in the course of several misfortunes, Dr Caius had been robbed of his purse. Thus the indisposed, queasy, and querulous doctor is ushered into the presence of Sir John who, no doubt well inured to liquor, is more composed. Most inadvisedly, Dr Caius plunges into a recitation of his grievances, thus: 'Last night you got me drunk; you violated my house!' This elicits the oblique response: 'But not your housekeeper', the implication being that this is a matter for which the doctor ought to be grateful, although he is not; he wishes Falstaff had violated the ugly old hag. Then: 'When I was drunk you emptied my pockets'. This accusation is directed, it should be noted, not at Falstaff, but at Bardolph and Pistol. At this point, Bardolph, also suffering a hangover, asks Caius to feel his pulse, almost the only professional activity the doctor undertakes in the whole opera. All this enables Sir John adroitly to escape from the dock and assume a more judicial position, whereat he wastes no time in pronouncing a verdict of not guilty: 'The charge is refuted. Go in peace!' At this juncture even the imperceptive doctor appreciates that he is getting nowhere, and he storms out in disgust, escorted to the door and seen off by the jeering Bardolph and Pistol and declaring: 'If ever I get drunk again at this inn, I swear it will be only with honest, sober, civil, pious folk'. How often have such resolutions been uttered?

This opening episode of the opera, brief, coarse, comic, and seemingly slight, is important structurally and musically.[1] The opera has no overture as such, yet that whole initial passage just described is a de facto overture with a most interesting key structure. Caius' prosecution is given the key of C Major, while E Major is the key of Falstaff's defence. Then, as Caius departs, there is a sudden switch into A flat Major, at the point where Falstaff advises Bardolph and Pistol 'Rubar con garbo e a tempo' ('Steal deftly and at the right time'), and, like the raising of a curtain, the opera proper begins, as Falstaff explains his plan to woo both Alice and Meg, the 'Merry Wives' of Windsor.

As has repeatedly been emphasised, doctors should not consume alcohol when on duty. The evidence of *Falstaff* indicates further that it is unwise of them, even when at leisure, to carouse with patients, albeit the latter are here but potential, rather than actual, patients. Dr Caius was professionally imprudent.

---

1. *Falstaff*. See Preface note 15. Vol. 3, pp. 445–9.

A MONK AS PHYSICIAN

PFITZNER: DER ARME HEINRICH 1895

Hans Pfitzner, who lived from 1869 to 1949, was one of Richard Wagner's earliest and most prominent operatic heirs. His music was upheld by the Nazis as being 'in the best German tradition' and they contrasted it with the 'degeneracy' of Richard Strauss, although Strauss had earlier enjoyed their favour. After the Second World War, Strauss resurfaced, but Pfitzner was discovered living in penury in a Munich home for the aged by the President of the Vienna Philharmonic Orchestra. He was taken to Vienna and supported by the orchestra.

Pfitzner's first opera, *Der Arme Heinrich* (*Poor Henry*), was completed in 1893 and premiered in 1895 to a libretto by the composer himself and James Grun after a medieval poem by Hartmann von Aue. That operatic libretto was written in a predominantly Wagnerian style of poetic diction, while the musical composition likewise, and particularly in Act I, has been seen as, especially harmonically, 'a landmark of 1890s intellectual Wagnerism'.

The German knight Heinrich (tenor) is seriously ill. In Hartmann's original poem the diagnosis is stated clearly to be leprosy; in the opera the malady is more vaguely, but distinctly disapprovingly, held to be a divine punishment for youthful wantonness. Heinrich's vassal Dietrich (baritone) is sent to seek the advice of a famous physician (bass), who is a monk at the monastery of Salerno. Dietrich's wife Hilde (soprano) and their young daughter Agnes (soprano) tend the sick Heinrich while Dietrich is away. When Dietrich returns, his grim news is that the physician has pronounced that only the willing sacrifice of a young virgin can effect the knight's recovery. This is a form of treatment which almost certainly would not be sanctioned by licensing authorities today. To the horror of her parents, Agnes declares that she will sacrifice herself to save Heinrich.

Heinrich, Dietrich, Hilde, and Agnes travel to the monastery for the sacrificial ceremony. Heinrich wishes to prevent this, but is too weak to prevail. The bloodthirsty physician confirms that Agnes is a willing victim, and he is impressed by both her devotion and resolve. Agnes sings a Liebestod before the now moribund Heinrich, then she and the physician enter the sacrificial chamber and close the doors. Heinrich, suddenly horrified at what is about to take place, erupts into action, batters his way into the chamber, and releases the still-living Agnes. A chorus of monks acclaims the miracle of Heinrich's recovery, they stretch their hands out towards Agnes, and the physician kisses the hem of her garment. The opera concludes as the music shifts from D minor into a transcendental A minor.

The medical cure must be taken in this case to have been effected by divine means. The date of the opera, and certainly of Hartmann's poem, was too early for there to be effective therapy for either the originally specified leprosy or for the insinuated venereal affliction of the derived opera. A psychological malady can probably be discounted. The heroines of Wagner himself often died suddenly and inexplicably. The abrupt converse recovery of Heinrich, hero of one of Wagner's heirs, Pfitzner, is medically as similarly mysterious.

AN EVIL DOCTOR

Some literary works or historical events attract especial attention as providing material which is particularly suitable for an opera. Thus the story of Romeo and Juliet, which appeared well before Shakespeare's play of that title, has been employed in many operas, as was discussed in some detail in Chapter 16.

Another of Shakespeare's plays, *The Merry Wives of Windsor*, has been adapted as an operatic libretto on at least seven occasions, listed in Chapter 41.

The 14th-century historical events surrounding Inés de Castro, the secret wife and mother of the children of Don Pedro, Crown Prince of Portugal, have likewise formed the basis of some twenty operas, of which the best known, all with the title *Inés de Castro*, are the three respectively by Zingarelli to a libretto by Gasperini of 1798; by Persiani, to a libretto by Cammarano, of 1835; and by James MacMillan, after the play by John Clifford, of 1996. James MacMillan's opera contains no doctors, but it does include a bass-baritone torturer (called simply Ordinary Person No.4) who enters into very lengthy and unpleasant anatomical detail.

OPERAS DERIVED FROM THE SCARLET LETTER 1850
Nathaniel Hawthorne's novel *The Scarlet Letter* has repeatedly been acclaimed as having a plot eminently appropriate to operatic treatment, a recommendation which not surprisingly has been taken up on numerous occasions. Derived operas (there could well be others that have now disappeared from view) include the following:

> Walter Damrosch *The Scarlet Letter* 1896 to a libretto by G.P. Lathrop.
> Avery Claflin *Hester Prynne* 1936, revised 1971, to a libretto by Dorothea Claflin.
> Michael P. Gehlen *The Scarlet Letter*. This was composed at some time in the 20th century, but I have been unable to ascertain the date or the librettist.
> Robert DiDomenica *The Scarlet Letter* 1986 to a libretto by E.H. Eglin.

Martin Herman *The Scarlet Letter* 1992 to a libretto by T. Curley.
Lori Laitman *The Scarlet Letter* 2008 to a libretto by D. Mason.
Margaret Garwood *The Scarlet Letter* 2010 to her own libretto.
There also exists a rock opera *The Scarlet Letter* with music and lyrics by Mark Governor, while the Terpsicorps Theatre of Dance has performed a ballet of that title.

It is certainly not difficult to perceive why *The Scarlet Letter* has exerted such attraction as material for musico-dramatic treatment. The story begins with a vividly compelling scene; proceeds via harrowing deceitful intrigue, which is apparent to the audience and to two, but crucially not the third, of the principal singers; and then concludes with a highly dramatic yet unpredictable dénouement. The medical profession does not emerge well; the physician here is probably the most evil and unethical of all operatic doctors – no modest achievement considering the highly competitive field.

The action is set in the 17th century in the town of Boston, Massachusetts, the latter then an English colony, and rigidly and oppressively puritanical. Hester Prynne has been resident in Boston for about two years. Her husband, who was supposed to have joined her, has not appeared, and is presumed to have been lost on his voyage from Europe. But Hester has, some two months earlier, given birth to a daughter, and hence has been, indisputably, adulterous. For this grievous sin she has been imprisoned. As the action begins, she is led out from the prison before the assembled citizens of the town, wearing a prominent scarlet letter 'A' embroidered by herself on her bosom. This scarlet letter, denoting her adultery, she is to wear henceforth.

She is made to stand on the platform of the scaffold before the prison, and is publicly denounced for 'bringing shame upon all'. She is formally entreated by the young clergyman, Mr Dimmesdale, a person highly regarded by everyone, 'to speak out the name of thy fellow-sinner and fellow-sufferer! Be not silent from any mistaken pity and tenderness for him ... What can thy silence do for him, except it tempt him ... to add hypocrisy to sin?' Yet Hester refuses to answer.

This scene is observed by an elderly stranger, a physician well versed in herbal medicine and going by the name of Dr Roger Chillingworth. He is in reality, and is recognised by Hester as such, her long-lost husband. He, to whom she also refuses to disclose the name of her paramour, vows to discover and persecute that person. The supposed Dr Chillingworth further makes Hester swear that she will not reveal his identity.

Of course, Chillingworth, and the audience, soon perceive that the unknown father is the young, widely revered, cleric, Dimmesdale. Chillingworth insinuates himself as Dimmesdale's doctor, prescribes for him various botanically derived medicines, and, while ostensibly offering professional advice and comfort, cunningly and progressively undermines Dimmesdale's psychological condition. Throughout, the evil doctor behaves towards the minister 'with the grave and intent regard of a physician towards his patient'. Dimmesdale is unwittingly obliged to endure this mental torture for seven years. Then Hester, no longer able to countenance the cruel deception, breaks her oath, and reveals the true identity of Dr Chillingworth to the minister.

The climax is overwhelmingly dramatic. The Reverend Mr Dimmesdale is, by general acclaim, invited to deliver, before the whole town, the prestigious Election Sermon. He gives a superb address. Then, followed by the populace, he leaves the church, gathers up Hester and their daughter, and all three mount the scaffold. And there, before the entire town he publicly declares that he is the father of Hester's child. Chillingworth joins them. 'Hadst thou sought the whole earth over,' says he, looking darkly at the clergyman, 'there was no place so secret – no high place nor lowly place where thou couldst have escaped me – save on this very scaffold!' 'Thanks be to him who hath led me hither!' answers the minister, who then duly and dramatically expires. Some librettists have the Doctor also dying at this point, although that is not specified in the novel.

It is readily apparent that this is a narrative superbly suited to operatic treatment. The three principal characters are vividly and contrastingly delineated: Hester Prynne heroically steadfast; Dimmesdale eloquent and devout, yet consumed by guilt; Dr Chillingworth evilly vengeful. All of this is played out within the cruel, rigid self-righteousness of 17th-century Massachusetts. There is a striking opening scene showing the public condemnation of Hester, and her dignified silence. Then follows the surprise arrival of her long-absent husband, with his appropriation of the role of physician, and hence slow tormentor, of the minister Dimmesdale. Finally there occurs the vivid resolution of the drama on the very scaffold where it opened.

There is no problem concerning the casting of the three principal characters, as usually soprano, tenor, and bass or baritone. The one significant operatic problem is the portrayal of the illegitimate child, a girl, Pearl, who is in the novel three months old at the beginning, and at the final scene, wherein she is with her mother once more at the scaffold, aged seven years. But that, as has been repeatedly shown by librettists and composers, is not an insuperable obstacle.

Dr Roger Chillingworth, undoubtedly, is a thoroughly unsavoury and unethical professional man. Perhaps, however, it is apposite to conclude this series with him. As we have seen, operatic doctors comprise a most disparate assortment. This one must surely be the most evil of them all.

ENVOI

In this account I have deliberately taken a broad, inclusive view of what comprises a doctor in opera. Even so, I have been surprised at the number of operas which do include a doctor (or 'doctor') as a character. More than one hundred of the 140 operas quoted in this volume concern medical matters.

My approach has also been explicitly irreverent, which is just as well, because librettists have often shown medical men and women scant respect; nor indeed should they. The doctors depicted here are distinctly diverse, personally, professionally, and musico-dramatically. One clearly very skilled surgeon, he in *La forza del destino*, has evidently been introduced only as a dramatic device and has but a very minor role in the opera. Another surgeon, Pustrpalk in *Šarlatán*, is by contrast central to the plot and is also highly accomplished, yet he has the misfortune to be professionally disgraced. No fewer than four physicians are surpassed professionally by an impostor in *L'amore medico*. The cardiologist in *Arlecchino* has his diagnosis corrected by a bystander.

Amid a profusion of variously incompetent, mendacious, or fraudulent general practitioners, Dr Ch'êng Ying in *A Night at the Chinese Opera* stands out in sharp contrast as assiduous, skilful, and conscientious well beyond the strict requirements of professional duty. Dr Chillingworth in the numerous versions of *The Scarlet Letter* is extraordinarily evil. Very differently, the scientific accomplishments of Dr Makropulos are, by any standards, of the very highest order.

I offer one final reassurance to the reader of these pages. Although bad doctors outnumber good doctors by some threefold, it is highly unlikely that any patient will have the misfortune to encounter the venality or incompetence evinced by some of the characters portrayed herein.

INDEX OF OPERAS

Adam, A. *Falstaff* 128
Albarn, D. *Dr Dee* 4
Argento, D. *The Voyage of Edgar Allan Poe*
    85–6
Auber, D. *Le philtre* 66–8

Balfe, M.W. *Falstaff* 128
Barber, S. *Vanessa* 58–60
Beamish, S. *Monster* 74–7, 122
Beethoven, L. van *Fidelio* 74
Bellini, V. *I Capuleti e i Montecchi* 61
Bellini, V. *La sonnambula* 41
Benda, G. *Romeo und Julia* 61
Berg, A. *Lulu* 13
Berg, A. *Wozzeck* 3, 72–4
Bergsma, W. *The Murder of Comrade Sharik*
    17
Bernstein, L. *West Side Story* 61
Birtwistle, H. *Punch and Judy* 92–3
Bizet, G. *Le Docteur Miracle* 96–7
Bloch, E. *Macbeth* 40
Borodin, A. *Prince Igor* 2
Britten, B. *Albert Herring* 121
Britten, B. *Paul Bunyan* 74
Britten, B. *Peter Grimes* 3, 7–10, 59
Britten, B. *The Rape of Lucretia* 121
Bruce, D. *Push!* 24
Busoni, F. *Arlecchino* 27–8

Castelnuovo-Tedesco, M. *La mandragola* vi
Claflin, A. *Hester Prynne* 132
Cresswell, L. *The Perfect Woman* 53–5

Dalayrac, N.-M. *Roméo et Juliette* 61
Damrosch, L. *Romeo und Julia* 1, 61
Damrosch, W. *The Scarlet Letter* 132
Deazley, S. *Dream Angus* 46–7

Deazley, S. *Dr Ferret's Bad Medicine Roadshow*
    1, 68–9
Debussy, C. *La chute de la Maison Usher*
    87–9
Debussy, C. *Pelléas et Mélisande* 24, 89
Delius, F. *A Village Romeo and Juliet* 61
DiDomenica, R. *The Scarlet Letter* 132
Dittersdorf, C.D. *Doctor and Apothecary* 5–7
Dittersdorf, C.D. *The Marriage of Figaro* 110
Dittersdorf, C.D. *The Merry Wives of Windsor*
    128
Donizetti, G. *Il campanello di notte* 10–12
Donizetti, G. *Don Pasquale* 78–9
Donizetti, G. *The Duke of Alba* 105
Donizetti, G. *L'elisir d'amore* 66–8
Dudley, A. *The Doctor's Tale* 82

Eötvös, P. *Love and Other Demons* 117–19

Garwood, M. *The Scarlet Letter* 132
Gasperini, A. *Inés de Castro* 132
Gehlen, M.P. *The Scarlet Letter* 132
Giordano, U. *Fedora* vi
Glass, P. *The Fall of the House of Usher* 87–9
Glinka, M. *A Life for the Tsar* 90
Glinka, M. *Ruslan and Lyudmila* 61
Gounod, C. *Le médecin malgré lui* 97–100
Gounod, C. *Roméo et Juliette* 61
Governor, M. *The Scarlet Letter* 132
Gurlitt, M. *Wozzeck* 3, 72–4
Gyrowetz, A. *Der Augenartz* 31–2

Haas, P. *Šarlatán* 15–17, 135
Handel, G.F. *Orlando* 4, 40
Henze, H.W. *A Country Doctor* 116
Henze, H.W. *Elegy for Young Lovers* 120–2
Henze, H.W. *We Come to the River* 101–2

Herman, M. *The Scarlet Letter* 132
Holten, B. *The Visit of the Royal Physician* 106–7
Humperdinck, E. *Dornröschen* 61

Janáček, L. *The Makropulos Case* 55, 80–1

Khodosh, V. *The Letter* 1, 33–4

Laitman, L. *The Scarlet Letter* 132
Leoncavallo, R. *La bohème* 48–9, 83

MacMillan, J. *Inés de Castro* 132
Massenet, J. *Cendrillon* 1, 21
Maxwell Davies, Sir P. *The Doctor of Myddfai* 1, 35–9
Mercadante, S. *Il giuramento* 61
Milhaud, D. *The Guilty Mother* 110
Moussorgsky, M. *Khovanshchina* 90
Mozart, W.A. *Apollo and Hyacinth* 74
Mozart, W.A. *Bastien and Bastienne* 2, 100
Mozart, W.A. *Così fan tutte* 94–6
Mozart, W.A. *Die Entführung aus dem Serail* 6, 7
Mozart, W.A. *The Marriage of Figaro* 7, 110–12
Mozart, W.A. *Der Schauspieldirektor* 7

Nicolai, O. *Die Lustigen Weiber von Windsor* 128
Nyman, M. *The Man Who Mistook His Wife for a Hat* 113–15

Offenbach, J. *The Tales of Hoffmann* v, 25–7, 77

Paisiello, G. *The Barber of Seville* 110–12
Penderecki, K. *The Devils of Loudun* 41–4
Pergolesi, G. *La serva padrona* 2
Persiani, G. *Inés de Castro* 132
Pfitzner, H. *Der Arme Heinrich* 130–1
Ponchielli, A. *La Gioconda* 61
Portugal, M. *The Marriage of Figaro* 110
Poulenc, F. *Dialogues des Carmélites* 125–6
Prokofiev, S. *The Fiery Angel* 108–9
Prokofiev, S. *The Love for Three Oranges* 1, 21
Prokofiev, S. *War and Peace* 90–1
Puccini, G. *La bohème* 48–9, 83
Puccini, G. *Gianni Schicchi* 49–50, 89, 101
Purcell, H. *The Fairy Queen* 4, 40

Raskatov, A. *A Dog's Heart* 17
Ricci, L. and Ricci, F. *Crispino e la comare* vi
Rihm, W. *Jakob Lenz* 3
Rojan, R. *Heart of a Dog* 17
Rossini, G. *The Barber of Seville* 110–12

Salieri, A. *Falstaff* 128
Sandow, G. *Frankenstein* 76
Sawer, D. *Skin Deep* 55–6
Shostakovich, D. *The Nose* 51–3
Sitsky, L. *The Fall of the House of Usher* 87–9
Sitsky, L. *Lenz* 3
Spohr, L. *Pietro von Abano* 4
Steibelt, D. *Roméo et Juliette* 61
Strauss, R. *Capriccio* 75
Strauss, R. *Der Rosenkavalier* 64
Strauss, R. *Die Schweigsame Frau* 78
Stravinsky, I. *The Rake's Progress* 40
Sutermeister, H. *Romeo und Julia* 61

Tchaikovsky, P. *Iolanta* 32–3
Tippett, M. *The Ice Break* 70–1
Tippett, M. *The Knot Garden* 3, 44–6, 70
Turnage, M.-A. *Anna Nicole* 57

Vaccai, N. *Giulietta e Romeo* 61
Vaughan Williams, R. *Sir John in Love* 128
Verdi, G. *Falstaff* 3, 128–9
Verdi, G. *Le forza del destino* 14–15, 24, 135
Verdi, G. *Macbeth* 40–1
Verdi, G. *The Sicilian Vespers* 104–6
Verdi, G. *La traviata* 83–4

Wagner, R. *Parsifal* 123–4
Wagner, R. *Das Rheingold* 55
Wagner, R. *Der Ring des Nibelungen* 120
Wagner, R. *Tristan und Isolde* 108, 109
Wagner, R. *Die Walküre* 61
Weir, J. *A Night at the Chinese Opera* 18–20, 135
Weir, J. *The Vanishing Bridegroom* 29–30
Williams, G. *White* 1, 3, 127
Wolf-Ferrari, E. *L'amore medico* 21–3, 135

Zandonai, R. *Giulietta e Romeo* 61
Zingarelli, N. *Giulietta e Romeo* 61
Zingarelli, N. *Inés de Castro* 132